AN *ILLUSTRATED*
HISTORY *of*

MEDICINE

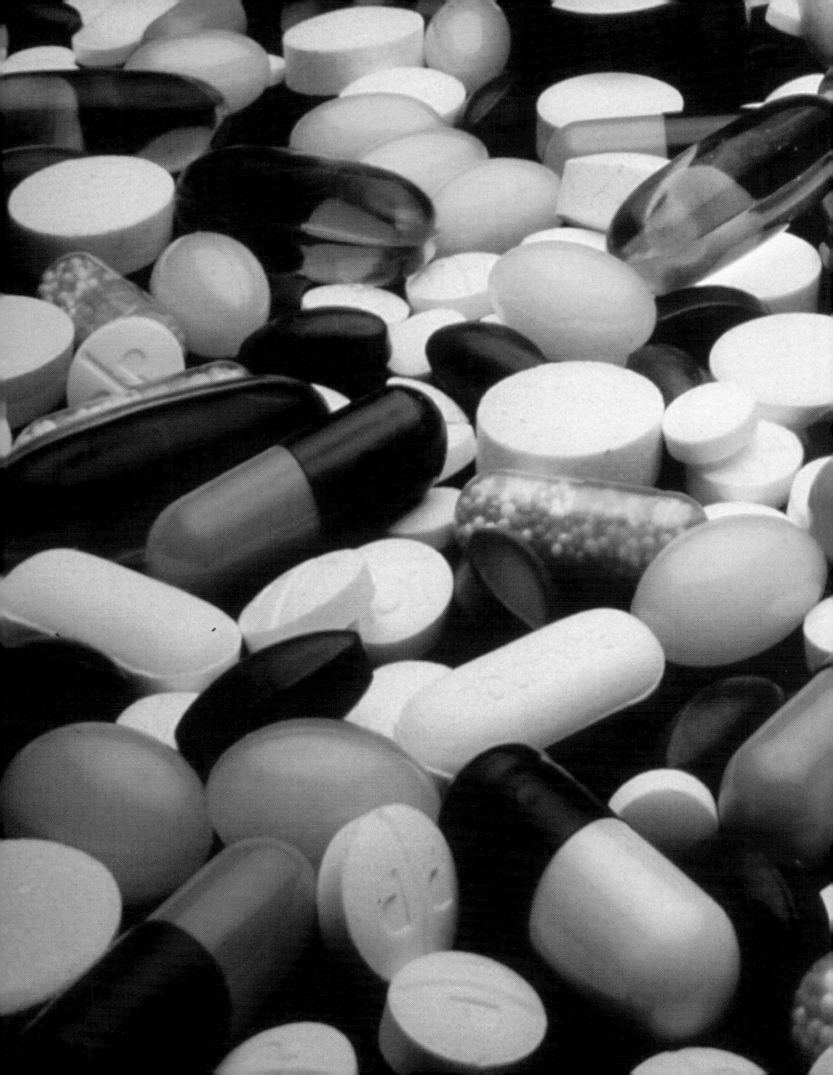

AN ILLUSTRATED HISTORY of MEDICINE

Jennifer Cochrane

TIGER BOOKS INTERNATIONAL
LONDON

The publishers would like to thank Michele Minto of the Wellcome Trust,
also Andrew Griffin and Marion Hill of St. Bartholomew's Hospital, London,
for their kind assistance with the research of the pictures for this book.

This edition published in 1996 by
Tiger Books International PLC, Twickenham

© Graham Beehag Books, Christchurch, Dorset

All rights reserved

Printed and bound in Singapore

ISBN 1-85501-809-8

Contents

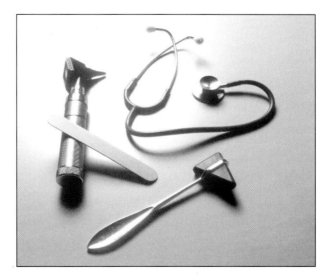

Introduction

One of the great differences between humans and the rest of the mammals is that humans, even from the earliest times, have attempted to heal wounds and diseases. Some other animals may lick a wound to keep it clean or chew grass to help with their nutrition, but if a disease attacks them, they can do little more than rest. Humans, with their enquiring minds and great curiosity, have tried to mend broken bones, cool fevers and cure sores for 12,000 years or more, since they could first be described as prehistoric men.

The art of healing has two main branches, one of healing by drugs and nursing, carried out by physicians (*physic* was the old name for medicine), and the second of healing by the knife, carried out by surgeons. Both branches of medicine are very old, and both have strong links with religion.

In many religions, the gods are healers; Christians believe that Jesus Christ was a healer, traditional Hindu Ayurvedic medicine is believed to have begun with Lord Brahma about 8,000 years ago, Egyptian doctors and physicians were priests, and healing gods were worshipped by Greeks and Romans. In some periods of history, religion encouraged research into medicine, whilst in others it forbade medical investigations. There has always been a link between magic and medicine, and in superstitious ages the line between healing and witchcraft has not always been clear. Indeed, there are communities in Africa, Australia and the Caribbean which still have witch-doctors today.

For many centuries no one knew what caused diseases. People believed that they had fallen ill because someone had ill-wished them or cast a spell on them; witches caused illness by sticking pins into a wax image which had nail clippings or hairs of the victim mixed with the wax. A comet in the sky caused a plague, and so did an eclipse of the sun or the moon.

It was not until the eighteenth and nineteenth centuries that bacteria, then called germs, were studied, and viruses remained a mystery until the twentieth century. Once the causes of diseases had been identified, researchers could begin to eliminate them. The two great weapons in the battle against disease were simple. One was improved public health – clean water, the disposal of rubbish and sewage prevented the easy spread of diseases. The other was the discovery of antibiotics by Alexander Fleming in 1928 – substances that killed or seriously damaged the disease-carrying bacteria.

Indian medicine is known as Ayurveda, which means 'knowledge of life'. Ayurveda is attributed to the Lord Brahma, the Creator, one of the Hindu trinity, seen here holding court.

In the very early days of medicine, people could not write, and knowledge of medical practices in other areas or even other countries depended on a traveller taking information from one place to another. What healers did must be deduced from the archaeological remains uncovered by historians, by studying their cave paintings and by looking at people today who have a similar way of life.

Other civilizations have left written evidence of their medical processes, and contemporary works of art often contain clues in writings, statues, paintings and illustrations. As printing became more common, doctors exchanged information through letters and learned journals, which historians can read today. More recently photography, films, television, videos and the Internet have spread information to a much wider public, assisted research, and resulted in the rapid growth in knowledge and technology.

Chapter 1

THE LOCAL DOCTOR

Today, anyone with an ailment in the western world either goes to a doctor's surgery or calls a doctor to visit them. A general practitioner, or GP, will examine them first. If necessary they can travel in an ambulance to a hospital where they will receive treatment from physicians or surgeons. One of the reasons that this is possible is because most of the population of western countries lives in towns or cities (many of which have universities where medicine can be studied). Other reasons are that the various countries have enough money to spend on medicine and that the population does not have to spend most of its time looking for food. There are many different occupations, people to run the towns and cities, to bring in food and sell it, to keep it clean and tidy, to be lawyers, teachers and doctors. Every area has its local doctor.

It is not like that all over the world. In Australia, the farmers who live in the outback may be hundreds of miles from a doctor; they contact him by radio, and he may prescribe for them from a medical supply kept on the farm. If the doctor has to visit, it may be in an aeroplane. The aborigines, on the other hand, give us some idea of the art of healing in the Stone Age. Their local doctor, or medicine man, wanders with them in their nomadic life, and uses traditional cures for any ills. The same is true with many wandering peoples, and is not so very different in remote African, Indonesian or South American settlements.

The local doctor is a general practitioner in western countries. This means that he has a wide general knowledge of ailments. He is familiar enough to take the terror out of a visit to his surgery and he can call on specialists' help if it is needed.

Prehistoric Medicine

In the Stone Age, people did not live in large settlements; they lived in small tribal groups, and wandered from place to place. The men hunted animals for meat, the women gathered leaves, fruits and roots for vegetables. If the group was lucky their local doctor lived with them; a member who knew something about curing wounds and diseases. Groups met occasionally, and medicine men and wise women could exchange and enlarge their knowledge.

As they could not write, physicians must have remembered the different cures that they learnt, and they would pass on their knowledge to a younger member of the group by word of mouth. They left very little evidence of what they knew, but they left evidence of their skills in tool making and carving, proving that they were both intelligent and practical.

When people settled down to live in one place, it was easier to collect and keep a store of medicinal herbs and to nurse anyone who was ill, and a particularly good bone-setter or herbalist had a permanent base and could be found if help were needed. Bronze Age and Iron Age peoples probably had a good knowledge of the medicinal qualities of herbs – better than most of us today. This knowledge was handed on through stories, songs and dances, and was buried in chants and rituals and became part of magical ceremonies. To a great extent they probably relied on magic to cure their ills, but they did have some practical knowledge of bones and anatomy, and were able to perform the very delicate operation on skulls to relieve pressure on the brain.

Above: The foxglove, *Digitalis purpurea*, is an important medicinal herb. The drugs digitalin, digitoxin and digoxin, widely used to treat heart diseases, are extracted from the leaves and seeds. It grows wild and the wise women who collected herbs would have discovered its uses. Today it is cultivated commercially.

Right: Stone Age man performed the delicate operation of trepanning, making a hole in the skull to relieve pressure on the brain. The tools must have been flint, and it would have needed a very delicate touch to remove a part of the bone without damaging the brain.

Australian aborigines and remote South American Indian tribes give us some clues about the ways in which early men cured wounds and illnesses, as did North American Indians before the onset of western civilization. Their medicine today is still a mixture of the mystic and the practical, and each tribal group has a medicine man who has been taught the spells and herbal remedies. Aborigines coat broken limbs with clay to help them set properly, chew particular herbs to relieve stomach upsets and cover wounds with leaves to keep them clean. It is very likely that Stone Age people did much the same. Bronze and Iron Age peoples were probably more like North American Indians, with permanent winter and summer camps and medicine men with a fair amount of wisdom, the women being particularly knowledgeable about medicinal herbs.

A medicine man prepares a spell in the privacy of his wickiup. He would have a sound knowledge of herbs and of bones handed down during the period of his training, but he would not believe that they would work without his spells.

Chinese Medicine

Chinese traditional medicine is very ancient, handed down through thousands of years, and it retains some of its historical elements even today. Chinese drugs include ingredients which western medicine does not recognize as having any benefit, such as ground tiger's bone. Poaching the decreasing number of tigers in the world for medicinal use has added to the likelihood of the extinction of the tiger, and is of great concern to conservationists. Not all the ancient remedies are out of place today, however.

There were simple farming villages in China by about 5000 BC, and by 1994 BC people were living in towns, building irrigation canals and beginning to write. Writing was common by AD 200, and a doctor Zhang Zhongjing wrote a massive medical book, containing all the medical remedies and treatments known at that time. The book recommends a preparation made from the horsetail plant to ease asthma. The substance is ephedrine, accepted by western doctors in 1928, over 1700 years after it was first described.

There is more information available about ancient Chinese medicine because the doctors wrote down their knowledge, and in China traditional medicine is still practised alongside western medicine. The ancient technique of acupuncture is now accepted as a complementary or alternative means of anaesthetising a patient or pain-killing throughout the western world.

As its name suggests, acupuncture is a system of treatment for pain involving the technique of puncturing the skin with small needles at specific points in the body.

This illustration from an ancient Chinese treatise on medicine shows mechanical cures for vomiting. They show that the Chinese doctors were well aware of the dangers of choking, and believed that the stomach should be emptied of its contents, in case they were the cause of the sickness.

手厥陰心包經之圖 左右二十八穴 凡九穴

This is an early Chinese diagram showing the acupuncture points of the arm. Compare it with the modern one on page 129. Apart from the difference in style, the information is identical. The technique has survived for 3000 years and is still widely used in China in modern surgery. It is an alternative medicine in the west.

There are ancient charts which show where needles should be inserted to relieve pain in particular parts of the body. It is not always needles that are inserted at these points. If small cones of a dried herb known as mugwort are burned at the same point, they have the same effect: this is known as moxibustion. Electrical stimulation at the same point also has the same effect. It is the points that are important rather than the way in which they are stimulated. Acupuncture can be used in childbirth and to relieve arthritic and other chronic pains, and is useful because it relieves pain without the use of drugs. In China, operations are performed using only acupuncture as an anaesthetic.

Ancient Chinese documents explain that energy passes round the body in channels, and that the channels are made to work more efficiently if they are stimulated at certain points. These points may be some distance away from the part of the body affected. There is no explanation for the effect of acupuncture at present, but research shows that the points stimulated may have an effect on certain substances produced in the body, known as endorphins: these are naturally produced anaesthetics, and it is possible that acupuncture releases more of them into the body.

Indian Medicine

Indian medicine, Ayurveda, is as old as Chinese, and Indian physicians also used plant products from herbs with animal products such as bone, horn, hoofs, hair and urine in their drugs, along with minerals such as gold, silver, arsenic and iron.

The local doctors were properly trained, and there were two great training schools for doctors: Taxila, where physicians were taught by Atreya, and Barnaras, where Susruta taught surgery. The teacher and the pupil worked closely together in these schools, the pupils learning knowledge, techniques and ethics directly from their tutor. Susruta left a book called *Susruta Samhita* which includes information on the development of babies in their mothers' wombs, human anatomy and a variety of surgical techniques. The anatomy is not accurate by today's standards, but the operations on eyes, ears and noses, the setting of fractures and caesarean operations are well described and successful.

There is a second great book which includes writings by doctors in the period from about 1900 BC to AD 1400. This book, the *Charaka Samhita*, contains a treasure trove of information about early Indian medicine. *Susruta Samhita* was translated into Arabic in the AD 700s to carry on the tradition of medicine through the Dark Ages. An important date in Indian medicine was AD 1066, when the best document on ancient Indian medicine, the *Charaka Samhita*, was written by Chakrapanditta.

The early Indian doctors made house calls; people were usually treated at home. The trained doctors from the Taxila and Barnaras schools worked with physician priests, who combined their skills with religious treatment. In 274 BC, hospitals for the care of very sick people came into existence. Unlike other parts of the world, women were not included in the nursing system; the nursing attendants in the hospitals were men.

Even at this time, doctors were worried about unqualified practitioners or "quacks", who were using poor treatments and undermining the work of the qualified doctors. This problem is still prevalent in India where there are a number of unqualified practitioners.

Ayurvedan medicine has not been superseded. Today there are 108 institutions in India teaching traditional Indian medicine, and the unique Ayurveda University at Jamnagar has postgraduate courses in traditional medicines.

There is another type of medicine in India which developed from the Greek doctors; Unani. This, like Greek medicine, is based on the theory of the four humours and elements, and on the belief that the human body is made up from air, earth, fire and water. Unani medicines are herbal, with some animal ingredients and others from mineral and marine sources. Unani can be studied with Ayurveda in the traditional schools.

Egyptian Medicine

Egyptians had a highly civilized way of life, lived in brick buildings in towns and wore beautifully woven clothes. They cultivated the land to produce food, and made impressive gardens. They also had a sound knowledge of medicinal herbs.

If you wanted a doctor in Egyptian times, you would go to the temple to find him. Egyptian physicians were priests, and spells were an integral part of their cures. They placed great importance on diet and hygiene, often prescribing certain foods to cure an ailment. They used castor oil, turpentine and opium, all of which are still in use today, in their treatments. Egyptian doctors left notes written on papyrus that have survived until today. For example, if you were complaining of stomach ache, this treatment might be recommended to you if you went to the doctor.

First the priest would prescribe *thwj* (presumably a herb) mixed with beer. While the patient was drinking it, he should say 'Here is

This Egyptian star chart shows that the gods were seen in the heavens then as the birth signs are today. The goddess of pregnancy and birth, Taueret, appears as a hippopotamus alongside Horus and Osirus. Taueret had a great annual fertility festival, held in Thebes. Infertile women would ask for help, putting their faith in magic rather than science.

the great remedy. Come thou who expellest evil things in this my stomach and drives them out from my limbs. Horus and Seth [Egyptian gods] have been conducted to the big palace at Heliopolis, where they consulted over the connection between Seth's testicles with Horus, and Horus shall get well like one who is on earth. He who drinks this shall be cured like these gods who are above.' The writer notes that the spell is really excellent and proven many times.

That is not too horrible a cure, but the one for blindness sounds exceedingly unpalatable! It is: Pig's eyes, its humour is fetched, real stibium, red ochre, less of honey, are ground fine, mixed together and poured into the ear of the man, so that he shall be cured immediately. Do it, and thou shalt see. Really excellent! Thou shalt recite as a spell 'I have brought this that was applied to the seat of yonder trouble: it will remove the horrible suffering.' twice.

These papyri, which also contain cures for diseases of the eye, the skin, the ears and teeth, and the diseases of women date from 1550 BC and were found at Thebes in 1862 by Georg Ebers and translated into English in 1937 by B. Ebbell. In 1550 BC magic was a large part of the cure, and Imphotep, who had been the doctor to King Zozer in 2600 BC, was by then worshipped as a god of healing.

Greeks and Romans

The Greeks relied less on magic and more on reason, as they observed symptoms of illnesses, made notes on how the disease progressed and recorded the results of treatment. They set up schools of medicine where people could go to be treated for illnesses, and case histories of the patients were kept in the schools to teach the students what to expect. The schools were often connected to a

Both men and women trained as doctors in Greece. This illustration from 500 BC shows a woman surgeon bleeding her patient, using a sharp scalpel and a great dish to catch the blood. The watching man seems to have a bandaged arm.

temple in which the god of healing, Asklepios, was worshipped. Asklepios had a family, with names that are used in medicine today. His daughter, Hygeia, for example, gave us the word for cleanliness, hygiene. The god's symbol, a serpent twined round a staff, is still used as a symbol for healing today.

Greek doctors knew, and used, parts of Egyptian, Arabian and Indian medicine; Alexander's journeys took him to regions where these medicines were used, and the doctors in his army profited from their travels, taking new information back to Greece when they returned home.

The theory that the human body was controlled by four humours was recorded by the Greek scientist Aristotle. This theory stated that the body had four main humours, or fluids in it: the sanguine – blood, the choleric – yellow bile, the melancholic – black bile, and the phlegmatic – phlegm. If these four humours were balanced, the body was completely healthy. If diet or the weather was wrong, or if the patient got too cold or wet, then the humours lost their balance and illness resulted. That was how bleeding became a treatment for illness; the doctor had to remove blood to restore the balance of fluids in the body. This theory continued for hundreds of years, and some cultures still apply leeches to remove blood from the body.

Hippocrates was the most famous of the Greek doctors and teachers, and is still known as the Father of Medicine. He was born about 460 BC and died in 370 BC. He set up his school on the island of Cos, where he was born, and where he taught that 'every disease has its own nature and arises from external causes, from cold, from the sun or from changing winds.' His honest case notes, his emphasis on symptoms and the natural course of an illness following those particular symptoms, the fact that the body could cure itself in many cases, and the importance he placed on handing on knowledge all

THE HIPPOCRATIC OATH

I swear by Apollo Physician, by Asklepios, by Health, by Panacea and by all the gods and goddesses, making them my witnesses, that I will carry out, according to my ability and judgement, this oath and this indenture. To hold my teacher in this art equal to my own parents; to make him partner to my livelihood; when he is in need of money to share mine with him; to consider his family as my own brothers, and to teach them this art, if they want to learn it, without fee or indenture; to impart precept, oral instruction, and all other instruction to my own sons, the sons of my teacher, and nobody else. I will use treatment to help the sick according to my ability and judgement, but never with a view to injury and wrong-doing. Neither will I administer a poison to anyone when asked to do so, nor will I suggest such a course. Similarly, I will not give a woman a pessary to cause abortion. But I will keep pure and holy both my life and my art. I will not use the knife, not even, verily, on sufferers from the stone, but I will give place to such as are craftsmen therein. Into whatsoever houses I enter, I will enter to help the sick, and I will abstain from all intentional wrong-doing and harm, especially from abusing the bodies of man or woman, bond or free. And whatsoever I shall see or hear in the course of my profession, as well as outside my profession in my intercourse with men, if it be what should not be published abroad, I will never divulge, holding such things to be holy secrets. Now if I carry out this oath, and break it not, may I gain forever reputation among all men for my life and for my art; but if I transgress it and forswear myself, may the opposite befall me.

The interior of the Temple of Asklepios, showing him as a god with a staff in one hand and a serpent in the other. This was built in Rome in 462 BC after the city escaped from a plague. Legend said that Asklepios, who was a Greek physician, appeared as a serpent on an island in the Tiber and warded off the plague raging round Rome.

contributed to medicine as it is practised today. He wrote several medical treatises.

He insisted that his students should follow a strict ethical code; they all had to take the Hippocratic oath, and doctors continued to swear this oath until recently. Doctors still have to agree to abide by the essential parts of it, and if they break those parts they are struck off the register. Doctors who are not listed on the register may not practise medicine.

The Romans were great admirers of the Greeks, and of their doctors. Many of the Roman doctors were, in fact, Greeks. Dioscorides was a Greek surgeon working with the Roman Army. He published a herbal known as *Materia Medica* in the first century AD and which was still in use in the seventeenth century. It listed the plants and detailed the ills that they could cure.

The most famous Greek working in Rome was Claudius Galen. Galen was born in AD 131 and lived for 70 years. At that time it was illegal to dissect a human body, so Galen dissected animals and transferred the information on the anatomy of, for example, pigs to humans. As each species of animal has its own specific structure, he made some mistakes, but he learnt a substantial amount. He discovered that blood moved in the body, but not that it circulated round the body. Like Hippocrates, Galen believed that the body could heal itself, helped by herbal remedies. Some of these remedies are still used, and are called Galenicals. Galen treated injured gladiators, and learnt from their injuries. He went to Rome to become physician to the Emperor Marcus Aurelius. Galen recorded his ideas and they lasted for 1,200 years, mistakes and all.

The evidence for the way doctors worked in Greece and Rome often comes from their works of art. This carved frieze shows a Greek doctor examining a young girl. The figure behind the girl could be Asklepios; he is carrying the serpent and staff, the symbol of the medical profession then and now.

Although doctors like Galen were using scientific methods to find out about human bodies, many people still believed in magical cures. Like the Egyptians, the Romans would go to the temple for a cure, to the temple of the Greek god Asklepios. They took stone or wooden carvings of the part of the body they wanted cured. One of these temples, containing many small carvings of heads and feet, has been found near a spring in Dijon, France.

Arabian Medicine

The Arabian local doctor was probably one of the best trained in the ancient world, and the modern local doctor owes a great deal of his knowledge to the rescue work done by the Arabs in the eight centuries after the final collapse of the Roman Empire. Medicine is indebted to the scientific interest in all its branches which was encouraged by the Muslims as their conquering armies swept across Asia, North Africa and south-west Europe. The written works of Greek, Indian and Chinese doctors were read and translated and taught in the many hospitals and universities built by the caliphs. No one was excluded. Christians and Jews worked with Muslims; the Arabs allowed freedom of religion and ideas throughout their empire.

While Europe was engulfed by battling armies, Arab scholars were discovering the writings of past teachers, translating them and making copies to ensure that the knowledge they contained was not lost. The Muslim religion helped this rescue operation, particularly in medicine. The Koran says 'and if anyone saved a life, it would be as if he saved the life of all people.' Doctors were honoured in the Arabic Empire and medical writings were precious.

Science was also encouraged; Mohammed said 'Science is the remedy for the infirmities of ignorance, a comforting beacon in the height of

This ancient Persian engraving shows apothecaries making medicine, boiling the ingredients together over a brazier. The jars in which the medicines are stored decorate the top of the picture; top right shows the liquid being stirred and top left shows someone drinking it. Persians, part of the Arab community, translated and recorded older works and helped to preserve their knowledge.

injustice. The study of sciences has the value of a fast; the teaching of them has the value of prayer.' With that kind of encouragement from their religion, it is not surprising that many discoveries were made. The use of Arabic numbers was an important step forward and made it easier to calculate and record measurements.

There were many important authors through the eight centuries following the fall of the Roman Empire. The man who probably began the work was Hunayn Ibn Is 'haq, or Johanitius, who lived from AD 809 to 873. In his lifetime he wrote 84 books on medicine, translating Galen, Hippocrates and Plato. He also wrote *Questions in Medicine* and *Ten Dissertations on the Eye*. Another author who left very good descriptions of hospitals was Ibn Jubayer, a great traveller who lived from AD 1145 to 1217.

Teaching hospitals first appeared in Damascus in AD 707, and the state built and administered hospitals across the empire in which famous doctors such as Al-Razi (Rhazes) and Ibn Sina (Avicenna) were chief physicians and lecturers. Apart from the hospitals, there were many libraries; Andalusia alone had 70 and the library of Caliph Al-Hakem II in Cordova contained 500,000 books – even before printing had been invented. Unhappily, when the Moguls in their turn conquered the Arab Empire, they destroyed many of the books and much of the wealth of knowledge was lost. The teachings could not be lost, however, and were passed on to students and to doctors from other countries. Today's medicine includes many principles handed down from Arabic medicine.

European Medicine

Europe between AD 500 and 1500 was in much the same state as the former Yugoslavia in the early 1990s. The orderly Roman Empire withdrew from its outposts, taking its doctors and medical knowledge with it, and the many small kingdoms that made up Britain, France and other European countries fought one another in their attempts to conquer new lands.

At the same time, Christianity was spreading across the continent, the Roman Catholic missionaries preaching a need to love one's neighbour and a duty to look after the sick. At first they converted kings, who adopted Christianity as the religion in their kingdoms, their subjects would convert and gradually another kind of order was established. By 1100 it was well entrenched all over Europe. Monasteries were built, in which monks preserved the knowledge from the past and copied out holy books to save the information in them. In this way the writings of Dioscorides and Galen were passed from the Roman armies to the healers of the first few centuries after Christ. Those countries, such as Spain, which were part of the Arabian Empire, led a civilized, cultured life but it took much longer to restore order further north, where Vikings raided coastal towns and kings struggled for supremacy.

People who lived near a monastery, or, later, a convent, had easy access to medical help. These establishments had infirmaries, hospices and lazar-houses to look after those who were ill. Lazar-houses were exclusively for lepers, who were kept out of towns and were forced to beg for a living.

Monasteries grew herb gardens and made ointments and syrups to soothe common ailments like coughs and colds. They may have had brothers with a knowledge of herbs, but there were no trained doctors readily available for everyone. Most villages would have a wise woman,

In the Middle Ages the people went to the monasteries and convents to find their local doctors. Great religious houses had monks or nuns with knowledge of herbal remedies and would treat the illnesses of the poor. This is the scene at the entrance to the Convent Hospital at Mont Serrat, with the sick and injured waiting to see the healers.

with a knowledge of herbal remedies, who would also help with births. The problem at that time was lack of information. Most people were still unable to read, and the constant wars and battles kept people at home so that knowledge could not be spread as it could in peaceful times.

The Beginnings of Science in Europe

Through most of the Middle Ages knowledge was preserved by the church, but it did not encourage research, and there was virtually no advance on the work done by Hippocrates, Diosorides and Galen. It was only in the Arab Empire that any progress was made. Britain was more or less united under William the Conqueror by 1086, allowing more peaceful conditions. The Crusades, to free Jerusalem from the Turks, began in 1096 and continued for about 50 years. They took armies, with doctors, into the Arab Empire and gave them a chance to meet Arab doctors and exchange information on medicines and surgery.

It was during the Crusades that the Knights Hospitallers were founded. The Order of the Hospital of St John of Jerusalem was recognized by the Pope in 1113. It cared for sick and weary soldiers, pilgrims and travellers. It has survived through many difficult times, changing when necessary; today we know it as the St John Ambulance Association.

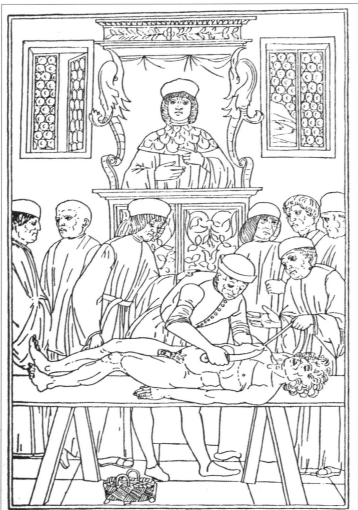

The University of Padua, established in AD 1222, was an important training centre for doctors for two or three hundred years. This fifteenth-century woodcut shows an anatomy lesson in progress. The professor reads from his book while a servant dissects a body, guided by an assistant. The students watched. Only a servant did the dissecting.

Modern Doctors

In Europe the training of doctors began again in Italy, when a medical school was founded in Salerno in AD 900, which taught both Greek and Arabian medicine. The medical school at Bologna was established in 1150 followed by the University of Padua in 1222. Padua was an important research centre for two or three hundred years. The training centres, helped by the invention of printing in the 1440s, began to produce doctors more like those we know today.

Italy produced important researchers as well as medical schools. Mondino de Luzzi, a teacher at Bologna, dissected human bodies and published a book in 1316. Leonardo da Vinci was an artist, architect, engineer and anatomist who also dissected, and in 1510 drew the human body very accurately, showing muscles, blood vessels, lungs and heart. He did not publish his drawings, and they were discovered later in his notebooks.

Andreas Vesalius, a Flemish doctor researching in Padua, published an accurate

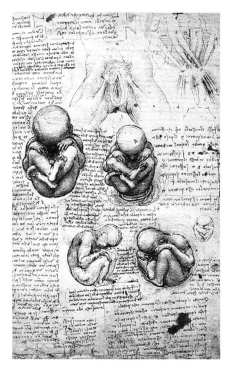

Above: These meticulous drawings of a foetus, drawn by Leonardo da Vinci, remained undiscovered in his notebooks with the rest of his closely observed anatomical drawings. It is only in this century that his work has been appreciated.

Some of the ancient treatments survived into the twentieth century. This photograph of blood-letting was taken in Norway in 1922. Country people still relied on their own cures rather than calling a doctor and were often suspicious of modern medicines.

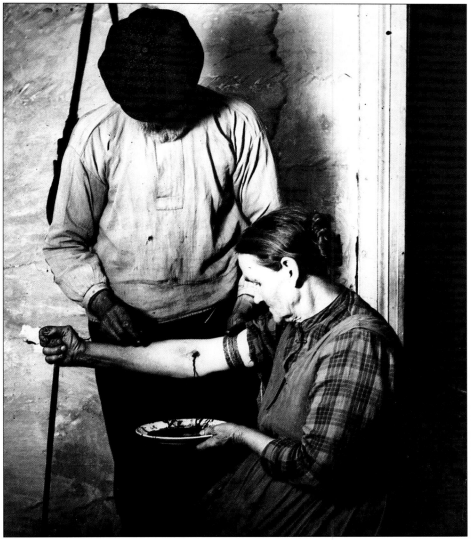

account of the dissection of the human body in 1543, the *De Humani Corporus Fabrica*. He disagreed with Galen and caused a storm of protest. He was a great teacher and his book is probably the most influential medical book ever published.

This was only the beginning of the career of a reliable, well-trained local doctor for everyone. Only very wealthy people would benefit from the trained doctors in the Middle Ages; others still relied on wise women, monks and nuns for cures for their ills.

From Superstition to Science

After the Middle Ages, scientific principles became more important in medicine, and people began to believe that something caused ills and diseases; before that, it was thought that disease was caused by demons or by ill wishes from another person. They did not realize how important cleanliness was to good health and they had no idea of how diseases were spread. Doctors did not look for a cause of pain and deal with that. A leading English doctor in the fourteenth

Cinchona was one of the discoveries brought back to Europe from the New World in 1492. The bark of this evergreen tree contains alkaloids which are still in use today. The best known is quinine. It was known as Peruvian bark and Jesuit's bark in the fifteenth century. The bark was soaked to extract the drug which was used to reduce fevers.

century prescribed this for the relief of toothache: 'Write these words on the jaw of the patient. "n the name of the Father, Son and Holy Ghost, Amen + Res + Pax + Nax + In Christo Filio." The pain will cease at once as I have often seen.' Not so very different from the Egyptian cure for blindness!

There were more doctors to help the sick, but they still prescribed bleeding, or drinks such as theriac which were made from very strange ingredients as a cure for many ills. As more dissections were done, more knowledge of human anatomy spread throughout Europe; more people could read and more books were published, and other scientists added to human knowledge, some of which affected medicine.

One such discovery was that of the New World by Christopher Columbus in 1492. He brought back Peruvian bark, or cinchona, (from which quinine is extracted), and mercury. Coca leaves, which were chewed by South American Indians as pain-killers, were brought back too. These medicines set off more lines of research into improving drugs. Opium was already in use and cocaine was extracted from coca leaves in 1856.

When Leeuwenhoek invented the microscpe and discovered microscopic organisms in 1675 it explained how diseases could be spread. After that discoveries were frequent, and doctors had more and more information to help them to diagnose illnesses and cure them.

Venereal disease was rife in Mediaeval times and people would try anything to cure it. Guaiacum wood was a fashionable but ineffective treatment brought from the New World. It was sold by street vendors, as shown in this print of 1519, and people consulted anyone who offered a cure. Unqualified men offered cures for centuries; in 1917 the UK passed a law making it illegal for anyone but qualified doctors to offer treatment and forbidding advertisement of cures.

Left: Patients in a mediaeval hospice, one having his hair washed, another his back massaged and a third being cupped. Cup-shaped receptacles were heated, then applied to the body. As the air cooled and produced a partial vacuum, the blood was sucked to the surface of the skin. Dry cupping resulted in a reddened skin. Wet cupping involved cutting the skin under the cup, so that blood was sucked out.

Below: This early nineteenth-century lithograph shows Broussais telling a nursing sister to continue bleeding a patient, already pale from blood loss. Broussais's system of dieting and bleeding was used in the cholera epidemic in Paris in 1832, so weakening the sufferers that they did not survive.

Hygiene was recognized as a way to prevent illness, and public health became more important.

Blood-letting, either by cupping or with leeches, continued to be a treatment for many illnesses until the nineteenth century. It is still used occasionally for particular disorders of the circulatory system. Herbal remedies continued to be used until chemistry was sufficiently advanced to manufacture the substances found in many plants. The discovery of inoculation and vaccination helped to curb the spread of diseases such as smallpox.

General Practitioners

As more and more information became available, it was impossible for a doctor to learn it all and still have time to cure his patients. There had always been a division between physicians and surgeons, but with

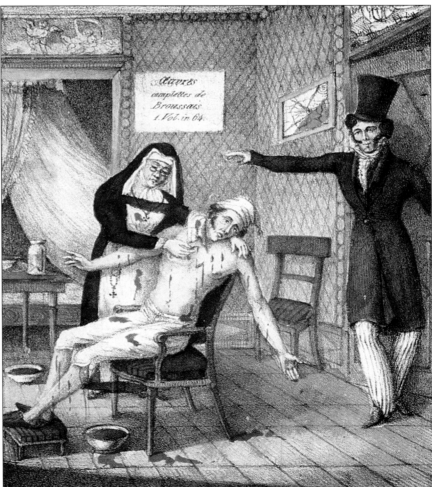

Above: A 1799 Rowlandson etching, lampooning a physician telling his unhappy patient that his treatment will continue. The patient is visiting the physician in his surgery; there are medicines behind him.

Right: A home visit from a woman doctor in the 1400s. The incense carried by the torchbearer on the right is intended to ward off infection.

more numerous doctors and discoveries, some of the doctors specialized in a particular kind of healing. There were those who were interested in looking after women, in childbirth and children, those who studied diseases of the heart and blood, those who specialized in lungs, or in ears, nose and throat complaints. These doctors were specialists; it was other doctors who knew which specialist could help a patient. The local doctor learnt the basic medicine, and could deal with simple ailments; he was known as a General Practitioner, or GP. If presented with an illness that

he could not understand, he would refer that patient to a specialist.

This system first began after the Renaissance, grew through the eighteenth and nineteenth centuries and is still in existence today. If someone was taken ill, they first called the GP. He would examine the patient, and might decide that an operation would cure the complaint, in which case he would refer the patient to a surgeon. If an operation was not the answer, and the GP had not enough experience to diagnose the disease, then he would refer the patient to a specialist physician.

In the 1600s there were six possible sources of help. There were a few highly qualified city physicians who had been trained in medicine and who charged very high fees. Alternatively, there were less highly qualified physicians throughout the country who could prescribe medicines and perform surgery, and who would charge about a month's wages per day. In cities there were surgeons, often not trained, who could perform operations but were not supposed to prescribe medicines. Every town had at least one apothecary, who had no formal training, but learnt simple treatments while working; apothecaries sold groceries as well as medicines. Every fair had a stall set up by a tooth-puller/barber, who probably knew quite a lot about herbs and who could do simple operations; these fellows travelled around the country, setting up wherever there were enough people to make it worthwhile, and they did not charge much. The sixth group were found in every village; they were the wise women and midwives, who either charged very little or nothing to help their neighbours. They may have had herbal knowledge from a local teacher, but no formal training.

After the Industrial Revolution, when more people moved to live in towns, doctors could look after more patients because they lived closer together and it did not take so long to visit them. Poorer people often could not afford to call a doctor; many doctors worked free in charity clinics where they treated those who could not afford to pay.

As the population grew even larger, and the state began to pay for medical services, the supply of doctors could not keep up with the demand. Doctors joined together in groups so that everyone who needed treatment was catered for, and the doctors could work in a rota, allowing them some free time. It was difficult for doctors to call on patients; those who were not too ill went to the doctor's surgery and only the very sick had a visit at home. By the end of the twentieth century, as computer technology improves, it has become possible for doctors to examine patients at long-distance and prescribe for them without a visit at all. Specialists can advise a GP without the patient moving from the GP's surgery. A new type of long distance local doctor could be the answer to too many patients in the twenty-first century.

A room in the famous Hôtel Dieu in sixteenth century Paris.

Chapter 2

HOSPITALS AND HEALTH

It is taken for granted in the developed countries today that anyone who is seriously ill will go into a hospital for treatment, and that as a general rule they will be very well treated and have a good chance of being cured of the more common complaints. Hospitals are clean, warm places with the best available medical help within easy reach. Outside the hospital, the crowded towns and cities are kept clean and healthy by the local public health authorities. People expect to be able to turn on a tap and have drinking water, to flush a toilet and remove sewage and to have rubbish cleared away from houses and streets. It has taken centuries for all this to come about, and in many parts of the world people are still struggling to achieve these basic necessities for healthy living.

Stone Age peoples had neither permanent homes nor hospitals; anyone who was seriously ill would have to keep up with the wandering group. If they could not, and were left behind, they would probably die. Because there were small groups of people wandering from place to place, they did not have a public health problem. They would leave one camp site, which would be clean by the time they returned to it, and because they lived in isolated groups and did not often meet other groups, they were seldom exposed to contagious diseases.

Bronze and Iron Age peoples lived in settlements and so could provide comfortable care for anyone who was ill. They did have to make sure that they lived near a supply of clean water and that the wastes from the settlement did not contaminate it, and they were in greater danger from infectious diseases because they lived in permanent settlements, but the groups were still fairly small and it was not too difficult to keep clean.

Problems began when people began to live in towns and cities rather than in small farming communities. There were more people producing more sewage and waste, and they needed a lot of clean water. Town dwelling started around the Mediterranean nearly 6,000 years ago. From the evidence left behind, the wealthy Egyptians had bathrooms, with great jars of water in them to use for washing. The poor people washed in the river, and their houses do not appear to have had any means of removing sewage.

India was better prepared. Excavations at Mohenjo Daro reveal that water pipes, baths and sewers were built in 1500 BC, although there were no public hospitals until about 274 BC.

Early Hospitals

For many centuries hospitals were linked with religion. Most of the major religions of the world make it a holy duty to look after the sick. In Egypt the temples had places in which patients could stay while the priests cured them, and there was similar sanctuary in the Greek temples. Alexander the Great built the city of Alexandria in Egypt where a university with a medical school was established in 313 BC. There the medical knowledge from Egypt, India and Greece was collected, and augmented by the learned men who studied there.

Romans, following the Greek example, built hospitals to look after their soldiers. They are recognizable as hospitals, with wards in

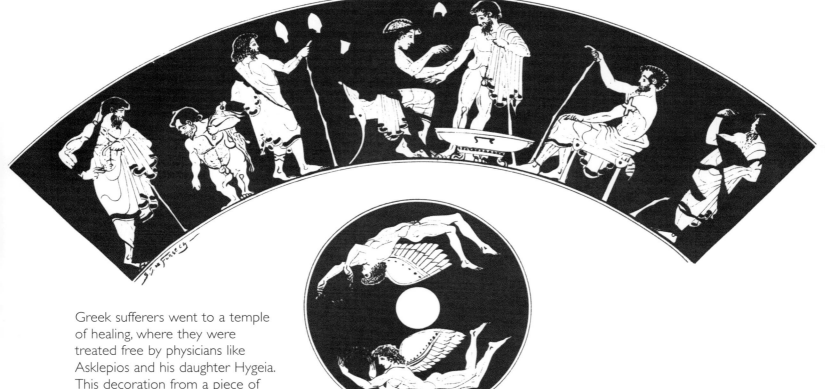

Greek sufferers went to a temple of healing, where they were treated free by physicians like Asklepios and his daughter Hygeia. This decoration from a piece of fifth century BC pottery shows a woman doctor bleeding a patient while others who have had operations, like the man on the left who has had a leg amputated, wait for a consultation.

which patients were kept and a refectory in which they could eat. Wherever the army went, hospitals were built, so that they spread over Europe. There is one near Düsseldorf in Germany, showing the layout of the Roman army hospitals very clearly.

The Arabs also followed the traditions of medical care laid down by the Greeks. They had teaching hospitals which were the responsibility of the state and which were inspected regularly to make sure that they were up to standard. The doctors were licensed and the care of the patients was excellent. After the decline of the Arab

Patients in charity hospitals were two or more to a bed, whether infectious or not. Here a patient lies with a corpse, which was not unusual in the sixteenth century.

Empire, Christianity took over the care of the sick in infirmaries and lazar-houses attached to religious houses. This principle is still evident today; there are still hospitals in which nuns nurse the patients.

Hospitals became more crowded as populations increased, and it was difficult to keep them hygienic. Patients would share beds during an outbreak of disease, increasing the danger of infection, and diseases such as tuberculosis and leprosy were common. There was no inspection to make sure that hospitals were well run. Some may have been very good, but others were positively dangerous. There was not always enough food for the patients, nor enough doctors or equipment to look after them properly.

The need to keep infectious patients away from others and to maintain clean bed linen and instruments was not recognized for centuries. Even in 1856 the Matron wrote this letter to the Senior Surgeon in St Thomas's Hospital in London. She said

Dear Sir,

The use of the ward kitchens for operations and surgical appliances has been a source of great discomfort to the sisters and nurses.

Possibly the surgeons have not fully understood that these kitchens are the general dining rooms for the sisters and nurses, that all their food is kept in them and that they are also used for the preparation of the patients' breakfasts, tea etc.

I hope that you will kindly bring the subject before the surgeons and that we may be relieved of this revolting cause of discontent.

I have the honour to be, Dear Sir

S E Wardroper

Personal Hygiene

As no one knew what caused diseases, believing that it was ill will or witchcraft that caused someone to fall ill, keeping clean was a matter of fashion rather than an effort to stay healthy. We do not know what prehistoric people did, but the later civilizations left plenty of evidence behind them.

Egyptians, rich and poor, washed themselves a lot. The river Nile was an important part of their lives, and they were used to building irrigation canals to water their crops in the dry months of the year. Even the poorest people could bathe in the river. The rich and the priests had water in their homes and temples. Herodotus, a Greek writer, described his findings from his travels in Egypt. He wrote about the priests: 'They drink from cups of bronze, which they clean daily. They are especially careful to wear newly washed linen clothing. They practise circumcision for the sake of cleanliness. The priests shave the whole body every third day so that no lice may infect them while they are in the service of the gods. Twice a day and every night they wash in cold water.'

Romans and Greeks were as clean. Men met at the baths then as they meet in pubs now. It was a social occasion; friends went together through hot and cold rooms, were

Right: The role of cleanliness in keeping healthy was well established by the beginning of the twentieth century. Underwear was changed more frequently and this French advertisement of 1906 shows that the idea of hygiene was a selling point.

Opposite Top: A statue of Hygiea, the best known of Asklepios' four daughters, goddess of health. She was always shown with a veil, draped round her on this statue, and carrying a serpent in one hand and a drinking bowl in the other. The serpent is about to drink from the bowl in this statue. Hygiea was worshipped by matrons, who cut off their hair and dedicated it to her.

Left: The importance of personal hygiene to health was not understood in the fifteenth century, and the architectural skills of the Greeks and Romans were lost. In this public bath house each patron has her own wooden tub and the water was poured in by hand. Food and wine was served! Most people could not afford to go to these bath houses.

oiled and scraped by slaves and could sit and talk over wine. Women went to the baths as well, to catch up on the gossip while they bathed. There were laundries to clean clothes and linen. Poorer people could not spare the same amount of time in bathing, but cleanliness was normal. Even in colder countries, Romans constructed elaborate bath houses. They also built central heating systems into their villas, with hot water flowing under the floors to heat the rooms.

When they left, they took their clean habits with them. The early Europeans were not as clean as the Romans. At that stage cleanliness was not linked with godliness; indeed some Christians never bathed at all. It was not until the nineteenth century that baths and bathrooms became a normal part of a house.

Early Public Health

While towns and cities were not too big it was easier to keep them clean. Egyptians, Greeks and Romans all had a system of drains to remove sewage, and water which was supplied by wells or otherwise brought into the town.

Greeks and Romans were good engineers; the Romans designed and built houses, forts, roads and cities particularly well. They made sure of a good supply of water and carried it into towns in aqueducts, and into the houses through lead pipes. Any overflow was used to flush through drains, which flowed first into a larger drain, then into a river well below the town. Romans also built public *lavatoria* and *necessaria*. We have mixed them up today. In Latin, *lavare* means to wash; a *lavatorium* was a wash-room. What we call a lavatory today was called a *necessarium* by the Romans. Perhaps that is where the word cesspool comes from; the two are certainly connected.

The Roman public baths were often very large buildings. In Rome today, opera and concerts are performed before hundreds of people in the ruins of the baths built by the Emperor Caracalla. There is plenty of room for both stage and audience.

All these skills were lost after the end of the Roman Empire, and public health regressed. Water came from rainfall collected in barrels, or from streams, springs and wells which were more easily polluted by

This section through the baths of Titus in Rome shows the succession of rooms at different temperatures. At the front the hypocaust beneath the floor keep the hot rooms at a high temperature. The laconicum, on the left, is rather like a modern sauna, with a hot bath next door, on the right. Behind is the tepidarium, which is cooler and behind that the cold rooms. Customers moved from room to room, first getting warmer, until they were very hot, then cooling off. They finished with a cold bath. Slaves would oil them and massage them. People went to the baths for a day, eating and drinking there and meeting their friends.

sewage from cesspools and drains. All the knowledge of aqueducts and pipes was lost. In the 1300s a system of hollow logs was invented to carry water between continental towns. There were baths in the houses of the wealthy again, but the water was carried to them by hand.

It was not until the nineteenth century that public health had returned to the standards set by the Greeks and Romans. At that time governments enforced laws to control the disposal of sewage in towns in order to protect water supplies, and towns gradually became more hygienic. By that time scientists had begun to discover the causes of diseases and realized that it was easier to prevent the spread of illness by cleanliness than it was to cure the illness itself. This was the beginning of preventative medicine.

Town, Country and Pollution

The tradition that people who lived in the country were healthier than those who lived in towns was based on fact. Country dwellers had more space in which to live, did not produce large quantities of waste and were more likely to drink clean water. Towns were usually based on a river, but until there was a proper sewage system and water supply, they were unhealthy places to live, particularly during the summer. There would have been cesspits to collect sewage at larger houses but proper sewage drains were not built until the nineteenth century.

Disease was carried by fleas, bugs and lice which were found on everyone in the Middle Ages. The crowded, dirty conditions in towns helped to spread them from person to person. This detail from a Van Ostade painting shows a woman searching a man's head for lice and nits.

Country people made their living by farming, which in those days did not cause much pollution. There were no chemical fertilizers, pesticides or factory farms to endanger the streams and wells that supplied water to houses and villages.

Towns, however, attracted the early industries. Apart from the larger population producing more waste and sewage, crafts like leather-tanning and wool-dyeing polluted the water. Houses were built close together and for many years there were no water closets. These did not appear even in the houses of the rich until 1596 when the Queen's House at Richmond had one installed, although Sir John Harrington had published a design for one in 1556. WCs were not in general use in Britain until 1778.

For many years people emptied what they called 'night soil' from their chamber pots out of their windows in the morning, shouting a warning to the people in the street below. The only drains were gutters down the middle of the streets, which drained downhill into the streams and rivers. Rain was relied on to wash the gutters clean.

This print from 1498 shows a woman emptying her chamber pot out of the window in the night, narrowly missing the revellers in the street below. The contents would run into the gutter to be washed away by the next shower of rain. Nightgowns were not used until much later!

As industrialization increased, towns and cities became more polluted by both human and industrial waste. Rivers running through large towns became so polluted that living things died in them. Writing about London in 1771, Tobias Smollett says: 'If I would drink water, I must quaff the mawkish contents of an open aqueduct, exposed to all manner of defilement, or swallow that which comes from the Thames, impregnated with all the filth of London and Westminster. Human excrement is the least offensive part of the concrete, which is composed of all the drugs, minerals and poisons used in mechanics and manufacture, enriched with the putrefying carcasses of beasts and men, and mixed with the scourings of all the wash-tubs, kennels, and common sewers within the bills of mortality.'

Rivers and streams can clean themselves, given time and oxygen, but the more pollution there is, the longer the process takes, a fact that began to affect the countryside as the polluted water flowed away from the towns through the farm lands, poisoning the water supplies downstream.

The crowding together and the lack of public health in towns allowed diseases to spread there very quickly. The speed of the spread of bubonic plague, or the Black Death, across Europe in the 1340s was helped by the insanitary conditions in towns and cities.

The Industrial Revolution brought many new pollutions to the towns. The use of coal as fuel resulted in thick clouds of smoke over conurbations, and stinging smog, which was a mixture of smoke and fog was very damaging to lungs. Industrial processes produced acid wastes which were simply released into rivers to add to their pollution.

This is an illustration from a book written by Sir John Harington, who invented the modern water closet. It was published in 1556. The caption was;

A godly father, sitting on a draught, To do as need and nature hath us taught.

Fishes did not really live in the cistern of the water closet; it was a device to show that it was water in the tank.

Monasteries and Convents

During the long period between the Roman hospitals and those of the nineteenth century, most of the nursing was done in religious houses. Great hospitals today owe a debt to the infirmaries attached to monasteries and convents. A great many still retain the names of saints, a legacy from the time when they were part of a religious house. The more modern hospitals grew from these infirmaries, which survived when the monasteries were disbanded as religions changed with the times. The monks and nuns preserved the medical knowledge through the Middle Ages and the Renaissance to give later medical researchers a starting point in their studies.

The care in these infirmaries varied considerably. There were those who were rather more concerned with souls than with bodies. Some clerics thought that it was a sin to worry about the body at all, and so they would not wash. There is an alarming account of the dead Thomas à Becket, who was murdered in 1170 on the orders of Henry II. Apparently the Archbishop of Canterbury wore a large brown mantle over a white surplice, over a lambswool fur coat, over a woollen pelisse, over a Benedictine habit, over a shirt, over a tight-fitting hair-cloth suit. All these were infested with fleas, bugs and lice, so many that the garments seemed to be moving. With this example it is not surprising to learn that the hygiene in the infirmaries of

Two different treatments for leprosy. In the lazar-house the leper is having his sores bathed. By the roadside another leper, represented as St Lazarus, has his sores licked clean by a dog. Most of the great monasteries and convents had lazar-houses to treat any sick travellers.

Right: In the past nuns nursed the sick as part of their duties to their convents. There are still nursing orders of nuns today and senior trained nurses are called sisters, the title for a nun. The nursing sisters dressed in their black serge habits, which were not often washed, and so were not very hygienic.

Below: The church forbade the dissection of human bodies for centuries but some doctors risked excommunication to find out what was under the skin. This sixteenth-century anatomical figure for students shows some accurate knowledge of internal organs.

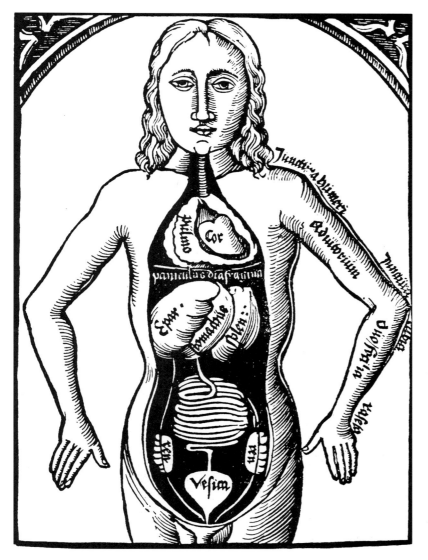

monasteries and convents was not consistent.

It was also difficult for doctors to find out anything new about the human body because the church forbade dissection. The translations of the works of Hippocrates and Galen were still the standard textbooks for doctors. Many churches believed that it was sinful to look for new explanations because God had ordained that things should be done in a particular way and it was going against God's wishes to find another way. This made research very difficult.

During the sixteenth century the Roman Catholic church began to lose its power as the Protestant religion gained strength. Some monasteries and convents were destroyed in parts of Europe during this period, along with their infirmaries, and it became necessary for secular authorities to build hospitals. In England the dissolution of the monasteries resulted in a reduction in the number of hospitals as well as schools for the poorer people. It took a long time for them to be replaced.

In untroubled areas, hospitals continued to be part of religious houses. As the power of the church declined through the seventeenth century there were many more scholars outside the monasteries as more secular people learnt to read and write; scientific research exploded, with many new discoveries in all the sciences. Printing helped the new knowledge to spread and, by the eighteenth century, cities began to found their own hospitals. Edinburgh was one of the first, building Heriot's Hospital as early as 1659 and following it with the Edinburgh Royal Infirmary in 1730. Monasteries and convents continued to help in the provision of hospitals, but they were no longer the most important part of the system.

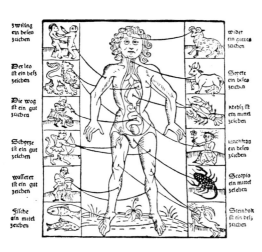

Superstition blends with science in this fifteenth-century anatomical figure. The diagram shows that the artist has seen inside a dissected body, but at this stage the heavens were believed to influence the organs. The students had to learn which star sign governed each organ.

Clinics and Wards

The movement from the cells and dormitories of the monasteries to the wards and clinics of modern hospitals was slow. One problem was that the learned doctors in universities were not the men who did most of the healing. It was the midwives, wise women, apothecaries and barber surgeons who carried on the day-to-day cures.

They did not read Hippocrates and Galen, they just prescribed the ointments to heal the sores, or pulled out rotten teeth or mended broken arms and legs. Through the sixteenth to eighteenth centuries more was discovered about anatomy and the causes and cures of diseases, but the knowledge did not reach the people who were doing the work. Treatment carried on as it had done for centuries.

It was not until teaching hospitals were established and opened their doors to everybody that progress in treatment began. At first there were very few of them, but as more towns and cities founded hospitals in which students studied patients as well as books, so more clinics were opened to which poor people could go.

The word clinic comes from the Greek word *klinikos*, or bed. Clinics were part of the teaching process: students would go with their teacher to the bedside of a patient and see the symptoms of an illness for themselves rather than read about them in a book. The doctors were in touch with the patients to a much greater degree, so the clinics benefited the people and the doctors.

Ward means a protected place or a guarded place. Poor-houses would have wards for sick people, as in the hospitals. As doctors learnt more about the causes of disease, they realized that some

In towns, surgeon barbers and apothecaries ran dispensaries, to which people would go to be treated. This illustration from 1550 shows tooth-drawers and surgeons at work, the latter lancing boils and bloodletting.

RULES
TO BE OBSERVED BY THE
PATIENTS
OF
ST. BARTHOLOMEW'S HOSPITAL.

ORDERED,

THAT the Patients shall be obedient to the Regulations respecting the Admission of Visitors, and that Visitors are on no account to drink Tea, Wine, Beer, or other Liquor in the Ward, or remain there longer than the time allowed by the Governors.

THAT no Patient go out of the Hospital without permission from the Physician or Surgeon under whose care such Patient may be placed, nor without the knowledge of the Steward or the Matron. Any Patient having obtained Leave of Absence must return on the same day, before the Gates of the Hospital are closed.

THAT no other Provisions, or Liquors of any kind, be brought into the Wards, than those which have been regularly ordered and supplied for the Use of the Patients.

THAT every Patient who may be able, shall attend the Divine Service on the Sunday Morning, at the Church of St. Bartholomew the Less, if not contrary to their religious principles.

THAT no Patient play at Cards, Dice, or Gamble, or Quarrel, or Blaspheme, or Smoke Tobacco in the Wards.

THAT every Patient must strictly obey the Directions of the Physician or Surgeon under whose care he or she may be placed.

THAT no Reward, in any shape, be given, by a Patient, or his or her Friends, to any Beadle, Sister, Nurse, or other Servant of the Hospital.

THAT any Patient acting contrary to the foregoing Rules will be reported by the Sister of the Ward to the Steward or Matron, and by them to the Treasurer:—such Patient will then be admonished or discharged.

Patients in Victorian hospitals were expected to conform to strict rules that governed their morals as well as their medical needs. Hospitals remained as strict as this well into the twentieth century; such concessions as parents staying with sick children are very recent.

diseases spread from person to person. Consequently, isolation wards and isolation hospitals were set up to nurse contagious illnesses.

Discoveries about the causes of diseases continued, including the revelation that scurvy was caused by lack of fresh fruit. In 1753 James Lind published the information that lemon juice cured scurvy and, if drunk regularly, actually prevented it. The Royal Navy eventually ordered lemons or limes for sailors on long voyages and cured them of scurvy. John Snow discovered that the dreaded cholera was spread in contaminated water, and it was found that mosquito bites, not bad air, caused malaria. Doctors realized that their patients' surroundings must be clean and that their food must be wholesome to help them to recover. Hospitals gradually improved.

Operating Theatres

The first hospitals did not have operating theatres. Surgery was associated with wars, and surgeons worked on the field of battle. Other operations were done by the barber surgeons who had no connection with hospitals. There was no special operating room; if an amputation had to be done it was done on the spot. No one understood the need for cleanliness during an operation. Patients were more likely to die from infection caused by the unhygienic conditions rather than from the operation itself.

It was not until the discovery of antiseptics by Sir Joseph Lister

An operating theatre in St Thomas' Hospital in London in 1920. Theatres were thoroughly cleaned with antiseptics at this time, but were not aseptic.

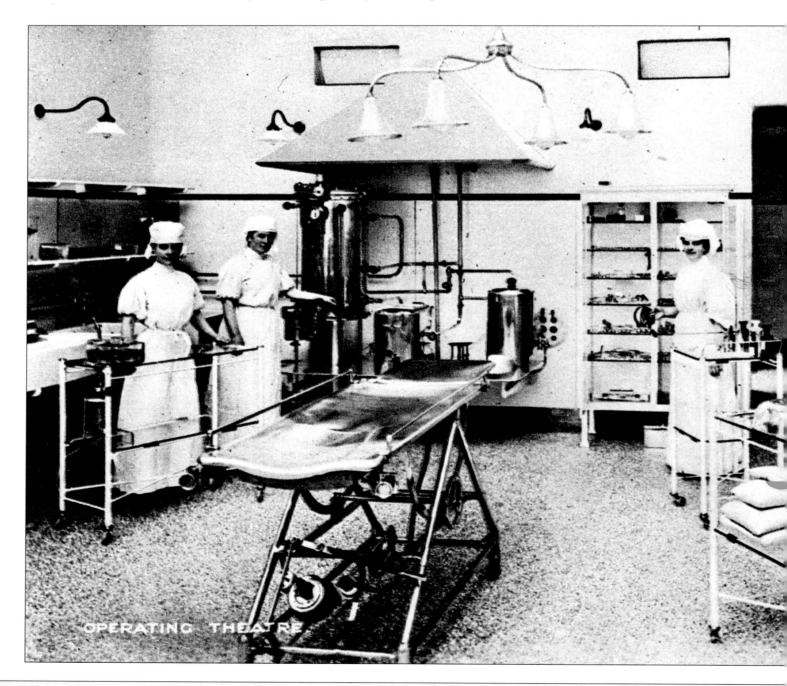

that the need for a special room for surgery was recognized. He used carbolic acid to clean his instruments and the surfaces on which he worked. Before Lister, surgeons would work in old coats stiff with the blood of former operations, and on wooden tables in which bacteria could grow on old blood and pus.

Rooms in which operations and dissections took place were called theatres because they had tiers of seats round them from which students could watch. The first permanent operating theatre was built in Padua in 1594. In London the Surgeons Hall was built so that anatomy could be taught and Robert Hooke designed a theatre,

Operations began on soldiers on the field of battle. Conditions were not even clean for most operations. There was as much danger of dying from infection as from the shock of the operation. This painting shows Ambroise Paré, using a ligature on a blood vessel to stop the bleeding instead of cauterising the wound in the sixteenth century.

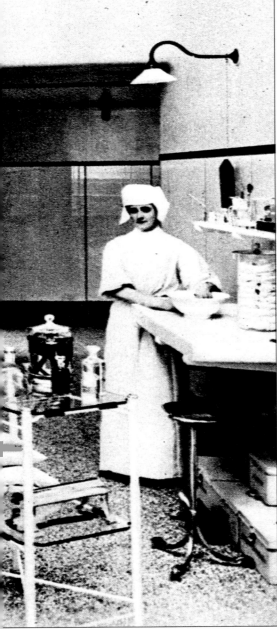

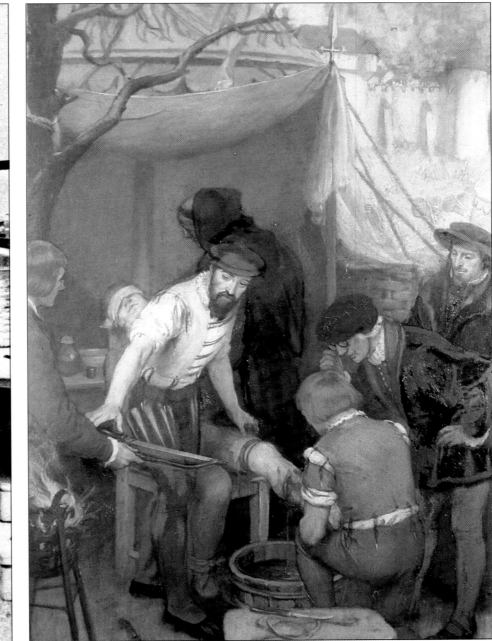

An amputation operation taking place in the home in 1592. The room would not be very clean, and the instruments used would not be sterile. In addition, no anaesthetic was used to dull the pain. The wound would be burnt with the hot cauterising irons seen bottom right. It is not surprising that many patients died from simple operations.

opened in 1674, for the Royal College of Surgeons. Edinburgh had its first operating theatre in 1697. These theatres became much cleaner after Lister's work, and were regularly scrubbed down with carbolic acid. Nowadays, onlookers are separated from the actual operating area by glass partitions.

Operating theatres today are aseptic, which means that no bacteria can be allowed into them and they are thoroughly sterilized after each use. Surgeons, doctors and nurses put on sterilized clothes and shoes before going into the aseptic theatres; hands are scrubbed and sterile gloves worn by anyone working in the operating rooms. It is no longer necessary to kill the contaminating bacteria as there are none there to begin with; operations are very unlikely to become infected today.

Right: Doctors who had attended lectures on medical subjects and watched operations being performed were issued with a certificate by the Theatre of Anatomy in Great Windmill Street, near Piccadilly in London, to prove that they had practical knowledge of the subjects.

Below: An aseptic modern operating theatre in which the innovative twentieth-century surgery is performed.

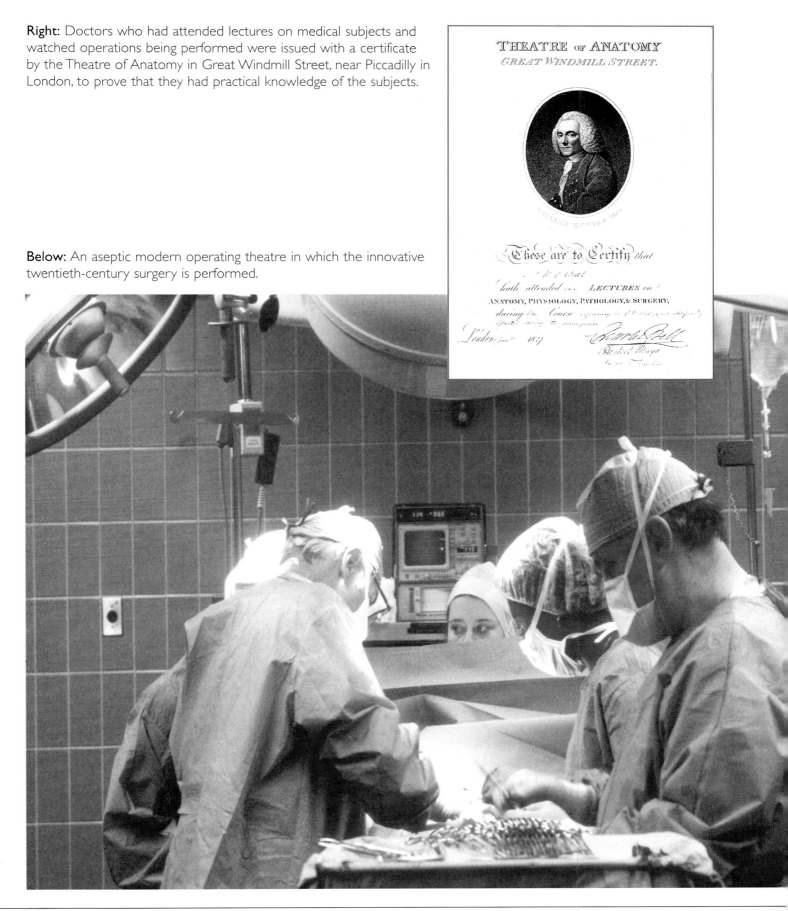

Chapter 3

REPAIRING THE BODY

Accidents will happen. They have been happening to humans since prehistoric times. Hunters could be attacked by the animal they were hunting, gatherers might fall whilst picking fruits, and, of course, there are always fights. Arms, legs and ribs may be broken, heads may be cracked, horns may gore and wound the body. Somehow it must be repaired, or the victim will die.

In prehistoric times, the victim very probably did die. However good the medicine men or the wise women, they had no way of replacing lost blood and not much chance of cleaning a wound so that it would not become infected. Animal horns would be very dirty, broken bones could pierce the skin, and knife and spear wounds would be contaminated with the remains of former kills, whether animal or human. A wandering tribe could not stay in one place for very long as it would run out of food; it had to move on, and travelling would not help the injured victim. Only very strong people would have survived a bad wound in the Stone Age.

As time went on, surgery and war were very much associated. Armies took doctors with them to look after the wounded; priests accompanied Egyptian armies, and Romans had specially appointed army doctors.

The armed services have looked after their staff right through the centuries to the present day, and there are now service hospitals, some specializing in wounds associated with a particular service. Air forces have special burns units – plastic surgery was conceived after pilots were first trapped in burning aeroplanes. Navies have units specializing in the complications caused by diving, and other specialist service hospitals treat the wounds suffered in their own particular branches of warfare.

Today a new set of problems has arisen; there are occupational diseases and wounds, resulting from the jobs that people do. These became more widespread during the nineteenth century, when factory machines and coalmines claimed their victims. Today, lung damage from asbestos dust, coal dust and brick dust and, even more serious, damage from exposure to radioactive wastes, have added to the problems to be solved by doctors repairing human bodies.

A painting showing William Cheselden, who published *Anatomy of the Human Body* in 1713, demonstrating dissection of a human to a class.

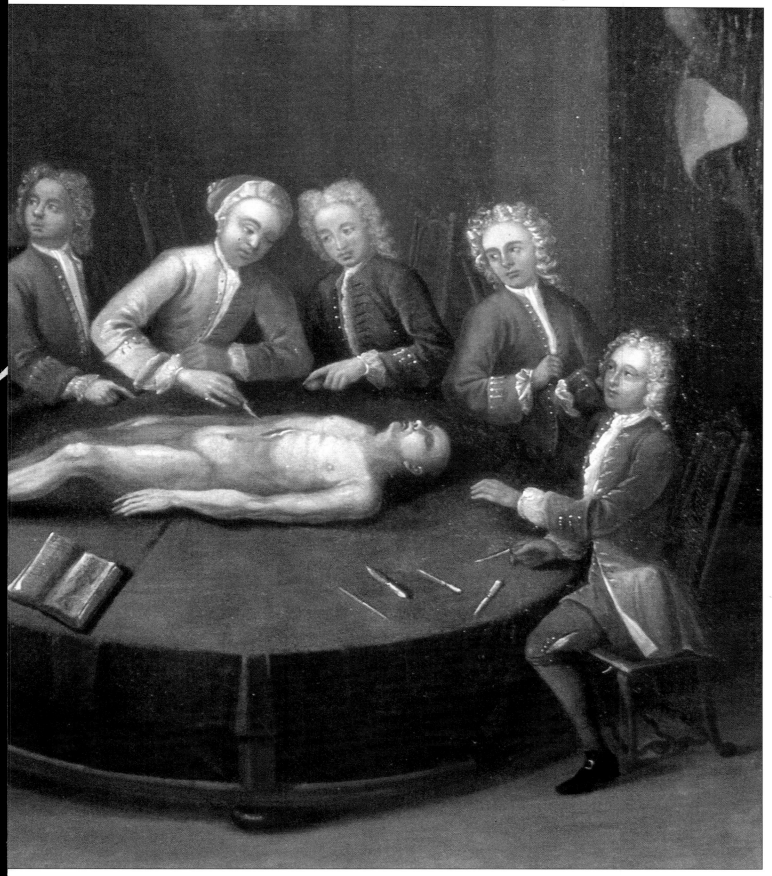

The link between early surgery and battles was a strong one. This sixteenth-century first-aid chart showing wounds commonly received during war was in Ambroise Paré's surgery. There are no gunshot wounds shown because the illustration is itself a copy from an earlier treatise published before the widespread use of gunpowder. The variety of weapons is interesting.

Ancient Surgery

It is amazing to us that Stone Age humans could perform surgical operations, but the evidence left behind in the shape of skulls shows that they did. Early surgeons from the Stone Age, through the Bronze and Iron Ages, from the Incas and Mayans in Peru and Mexico to Europe, trepanned skulls.

Trepanning is the operation that makes a neat round hole in the skull to release pressure on the brain. Trephining is a similar operation with a more sophisticated three-leafed tool.

The earliest examples are from 10,000 BC when the tools used would have been made of flint. Skulls from Babylon in 3000 BC have been found with holes in them. Some scientists believed that these holes were made after death to release the spirit from the body, but the holes show rounded growth at the edges, indicating that the owner of the skull continued to live and grow after the operation.

By 2000 BC there is evidence from writings and pictures, showing that bronze lancets were used to open abscesses, and that a fee of 10 shekels of silver should be paid to a surgeon who saved a life or the sight of an eye. Hammurabi the law-giver wrote a code of medical practice to guide surgeons.

In 2600 BC, King Zozer's doctor Imphotep, the supposed author of a papyrus discovered by Edwin Smith, records that the pulse was important in assessing patients and that wounds should be probed to discover their depth. Wound closure and splinting of broken limbs are also described. Imphotep was worshipped later as a god.

Since Egyptians opened their dead and removed the viscera to fill the interior with preservative spices, it was likely that they knew something about the internal organs of the human body, although accounts from the Ebers Papyrus from 1500 BC throw some doubt on their powers of observation. This lists four vessels to the nostrils, two for blood and two for mucus, four to the two ears, four to the liver, carrying fluid and air, and four to the lungs and spleen. It was forbidden to cut up the organs in case they were needed in the next world, which could explain some of the confusion.

The Greeks did not leave anatomical knowledge to chance. Homer describes wounds accurately and explains how to remove foreign bodies from them and how to stop bleeding. Hippocrates describes surgical instruments such as knives, forceps, trephines and specula. Dissection was allowed in the teaching centre at Alexandria, where surgeons were trained. The Greeks also believed in clinical observation.

Left: Trepanning and trephining is an operation dating from prehistoric times. It involves drilling a hole through the bone of the skull to relieve pressure on the brain. This illustration comes from a book on surgery published in 1573.

Below: The Egyptians preserved the bodies of their dead by removing the internal organs and filling the space with bitumen. They knew what the organs looked like from the outside, but were forbidden to cut into them in case the body needed them in the after life. They were very successful at mummifying; this is the mummy of Ramses II, who lived from about 1304-1237 BC.

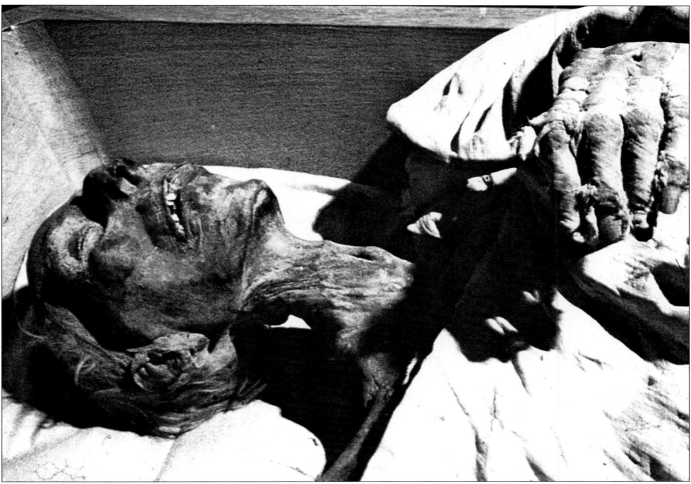

Anatomy Through the Ages

The Roman Empire, with its army hospitals, had a considerable knowledge of surgery, and this was recorded by Celsus and translated into Latin in AD 30. He wrote several medical books, and described how fractures with the bone through the skin were repaired and how several abdominal operations were performed. He also discussed breast cancer and when to operate.

Galen, whose work was used for centuries, described many operations, including tracheotomy, for relieving breathing difficulties and treatment of a punctured lung. These operations were not performed with any pain-killers; these had not been discovered in the west, although Hua T'o, in China, was using opiates to reduce pain and allow more complex operations in the second century AD.

The knowledge acquired by the Greeks would have been lost after the end of the Roman Empire, but for the Arabic teaching schools. They preserved the work of the Greeks and added to them. Mohammadan traditions were preserved in Jundishapur and continued in Baghdad, where Rhazes and later Avicenna worked. Rhazes recorded using catgut for suturing wounds and Avicenna used

The title page of one of the 240 editions of the *Regimen Sanitatis*, first published by the Monte Cassino Monastery in 1170. The Italians were influenced by the Arabic writings brought back to Europe by the returning crusaders.

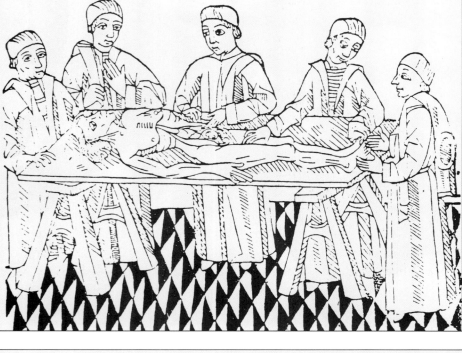

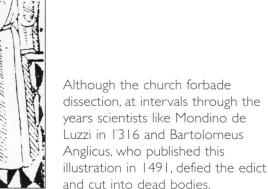

Although the church forbade dissection, at intervals through the years scientists like Mondino de Luzzi in 1316 and Bartolomeus Anglicus, who published this illustration in 1491, defied the edict and cut into dead bodies.

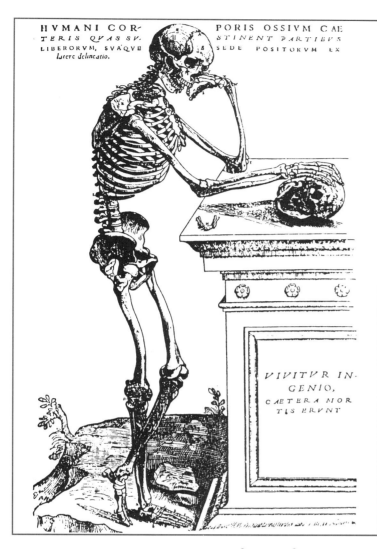

Diagram of a skeleton drawn by Vesalius and published in 1543. It is very accurate. The inscription on the tomb reads 'Man's spirit lives. The rest is Death's portion'.

Above: Andreas Vesalius (1514-1564) was a Flemish anatomist who first studied at and then became a demonstrator of anatomy in Padua. He held unorthodox views, based on his own observations rather than ancient writings.

forceps for removing a dead foetus. Unfortunately, Avicenna believed that surgeons were less important than physicians, and his influence lasted for almost ten centuries.

Progress in surgery was retarded by the beliefs of the church in Europe during the Middle Ages. Excessive modesty was fashionable and it was considered to be indecent to expose the body for surgery. Dissection was forbidden and research was frowned upon. The works of Galen, who had dissected animals rather than humans, were regarded as almost sacred. For several hundred years there was very little development in European medicine.

Changes began when Arab influences came to Europe with extension of the Arab Empire and the Crusades. Medical schools were established at Salerno in 900 and the Monte Cassino Monastery in 1066; Arabic writings were examined there. The *Regimen Sanitatis Salernitanum* and the *Practica Chirurgiae* were published by the monastery in 1170, the latter being an important reference work on head wounds and diseases of the neck and limbs for 150 years.

The next major advance in anatomy and surgery came in the

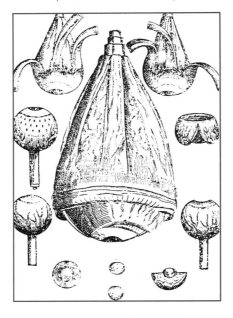

An illustration of a dissection of an eye, showing the muscles and nerves, published in 1583. The invention of a printing process made it possible to produce books describing and illustrating the anatomy of the human body.

sixteenth century, when Vesalius was researching in Padua and Ambroise Paré was practising as a surgeon in Paris. Vesalius shocked the medical world by disagreeing with the writings of Galen. Paré also caused consternation because he was a barber surgeon, with great practical experience in surgery but no knowledge of Greek and Latin.

Paré had been an army surgeon, treating wounds on the field of battle. He observed that wounds treated in the traditional way, by cauterizing them with boiling oil, festered and took a long time to heal, while wounds with a simple dressing on them healed cleanly. He also discovered that cauterizing bleeding blood vessels did not heal them as quickly as ligaturing them, or tying them up. His most important contribution was to convince the physicians that they might benefit from barber surgeons' knowledge. He was not accepted in Paris at first, but his successful treatment of wounds resulted in a long service to medicine, surviving through five reigns. He also designed artificial limbs.

Vesalius was an academic, a professor at Padua. He dissected human bodies and found that many of Galen's conclusions about the human body, drawn from his dissections of pigs, were wrong. He published *De Humani Corporis Fabrica*, with accurate anatomical drawings, in 1543.

Leonardo da Vinci had produced equally accurate drawings in 1510, but they were in private notebooks and so Vesalius knew nothing about them.

Padua was a famous teaching centre, and William Harvey left Cambridge to study there in the early seventeenth century. Using scientific methods, Harvey

William Harvey (1578-1657) was a British doctor who discovered the circulation of the blood. His discovery began scientific medicine; he demonstrated with animals how the heart acted as a pump to move blood round the body. He is seen here using a deer to demonstrate the blood system.

investigated the circulation of the blood through experiments on dogs. He discovered the difference between arteries and veins, how the heart worked like a pump and how blood passed through the lungs and changed colour there. He began work in 1616 and published his results in 1628.

Once researchers began looking at actual bodies and dissecting them rather than reading books about them, medical knowledge began to increase quickly. Researchers published drawings of their dissections and surgery ceased to be regarded as a lesser science.

The church was still opposing anatomical research, but in England in 1540 barber surgeons were given permission to dissect four bodies a year. The demand for bodies was considerable and this number was not sufficient; illegal dissections were carried out. The bodies were provided by grave robbers, or resurrectionists, who found out when a burial had taken place and dug up the body at night to deliver to surgeons for research. This practice continued for several centuries in both Britain and America. The grave robbers actually played an important part in the teaching of anatomy. Some went too far; William Burke was hanged in 1829 for murdering William Hare's lodgers and selling their bodies to surgeons in Edinburgh.

With more bodies to dissect, surgery made another great step forward. Doctors generally had accepted that surgery could repair broken limbs, wounds and similar damage to the outside of the body, but they believed that internal pain was caused by unbalanced humours. They did not realize that some internal pains could be cured by surgery rather than by medicines. Investigation of dead bodies revealed that damage could be internal as well as external, and could be repaired by surgery.

Grave robbers are regarded as ghoulish opportunists, but they made a considerable contribution to medical science. Without the bodies they stole, surgeons would not have been able to make any advances in their knowledge of human anatomy.

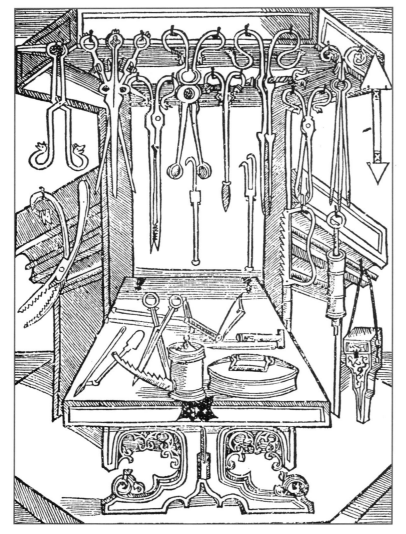

Surgical Instruments and Techniques

Once the structure of the normal human body was familiar to surgeons, they could identify abnormalities and set about correcting them. As more surgeons were trained and took up practice, new operations were discovered and new instruments were invented to perform them. The surgical instruments became more sophisticated.

The first surgical instruments were not unlike carpenters' tools. There were knives for cutting flesh, saws for cutting bone, needles for sewing up wounds, pincers, forceps, cauterizing irons to stop bleeding, probes, hooks and hammers. There were the same instruments in different shapes to be used on different parts of the body. Once Ambroise Paré's ideas for ligaturing wounds instead of cauterizing them had been adopted, animal tissues made from intestines or pigs' bristles were used to tie-off blood vessels,.

As surgeons grew more confident, it became clear that it was the pain resulting

If these two illustrations, about 300 years apart, are anything to go by, surgeons' tools did not change much in that time. The forceps, saws and knives in the Mediaeval woodcut above are very like those depicted in the Georgian painting. The variety of shapes of forceps and knives are for operating on different parts of the body. More have been developed in the later picture.

from surgery and the danger of infection afterwards that was holding back more complicated repairs to the body. It was not until the use of effective anaesthetics removed the pain, and patient, doctor, instruments and operating theatres were all completely sterile that surgery could take its next step.

The discovery of X-rays by Willhelm Roentgen in 1895 made a great difference for surgeons. They could then look inside a patient to see what was wrong, examining broken bones, for example. Unhappily, the dangers of X-rays were not known until many of those working with them died of radiation. Today both the operators and the patients are protected from too much exposure.

Above Right: This X-ray cannon of the 1920s helped to produce pictures of internal organs such as the heart and kidney, enabling doctors to diagnose ailments without surgery. However, both patients and operators were exposed to four dangers according to a writer of the time; acute dermatitis, chronic dermatitis, late manifestations and sterility. We now know that they were also in danger of contracting cancer.

Right: These elaborate amputation saws of the sixteenth and eighteenth centuries are not designed for easy cleaning. Note the patterning which would hold old blood and flesh and increase the danger of infection.

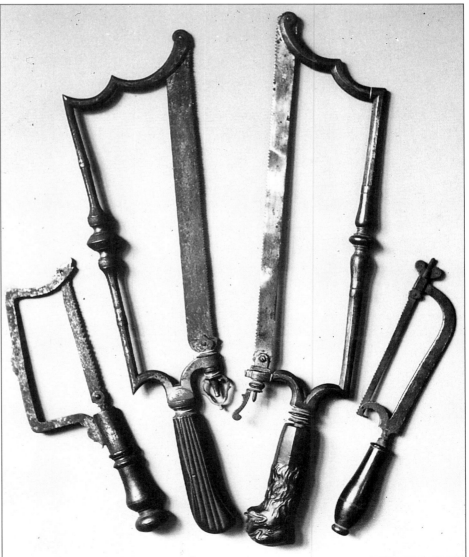

One problem with surgery is that it is either performed after an accident in which the patient has lost a lot of blood, or the surgeon has to make incisions during the operation. In either event, the patient loses blood.

Blood transfusion had first been tried in the seventeenth century, using dogs. Various experiments were attempted, giving people animal's blood or another person's blood, but these were not safe until Laudois discovered that blood from one animal clots when mixed with the serum of another.

More research showed that there were three common blood groups, but they could not be mixed with one another. Blood types A, B and O were identified, and work done during the Second World War means that patients today can safely be given blood of the same type during an operation.

Once surgeons could operate in aseptic conditions on pain-free patients, many more operations were possible, and with efficient blood transfusion to replace lost blood,

Right: Proof that surgeons' instruments were similar to household implements. This Regency cartoon shows a woman attacking her corns with a kitchen knife and some scissors.

Opposite Top: An experiment performed by Dr Denis in Paris in 1667, transferring sheep's blood to a man. It did not work.

Left: An illustration from a manual of surgery published in 1874 in Paris. This was the 8th edition of the book, obviously a popular work with doctors. It shows that methods of amputation had not changed much since Ambroise Paré, although the patient is on a special bed.

long and complex operations became feasible; open heart surgery, microsurgery and organ transplants are now commonplace. Great improvements in microscopes revealed the microscopic structure of human tissues, and new specialities of vascular surgery, neurosurgery and keyhole surgery have been made possible by lasers and fibre optics. Today, surgeons try to do as little damage to surrounding tissues as possible so that a patient can recover from an operation more quickly.

Anaesthetics

There are two types of pain-killers in use today, analgesics and anaesthetics. Analgesics, such as aspirin and paracetamol, dull pain and can be used at home for toothache or headaches. Anaesthetics are administered by a specialist doctor, an anaesthetist. There are two kinds of anaesthetic, a general anaesthetic that puts a patient to sleep and a local anaesthetic that kills the pain in one area for long enough for an operation to be completed. Dentists use local anaesthetics to kill pain while they are filling cavities in teeth. Doctors use them for minor surgery, such as sewing up a cut or removing a wart.

Pain-killers have been known for centuries. Both the Chinese and the Egyptians used opium and the South American Indians chewed coca leaves and spread the juice on their wounds to dull pain, and alcohol has been used for centuries – but none of these methods was completely effective. Good surgeons were fast surgeons before anaesthetics were discovered. The Swiss physician Paracelsus used a pain-killer made with opium, which he called laudanum, in the early sixteenth century, which was taken for headaches until the present century.

In 1806 the German pharmacologist Friedrich Serturner discovered morphine, a compound of opium. Morphine is a powerful pain-killer, but is also a dangerously addictive drug. It is used today, but with great care.

Local anaesthesia was first used in 1812 by Napoleon's surgeon, Baron Larrey. During Napoleon's retreat from Moscow he amputated limbs painlessly by freezing them.

Below Left: The introduction of anaesthetics made the shock to patients much less. Chloroform was first used in 1847. Here a doctor drips chloroform onto a gauze cone over the patient's nose during an operation at St Bartholomew's Hospital in London.

Below: The administration of chloroform from a bag suspended behind the doctor, a mixture of gas and air breathed in through a rubber cone over the nose.

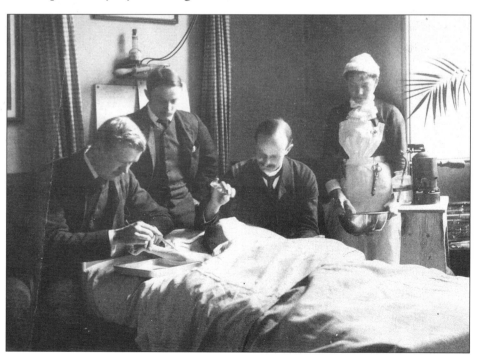

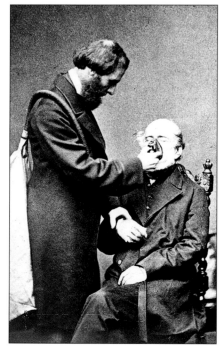

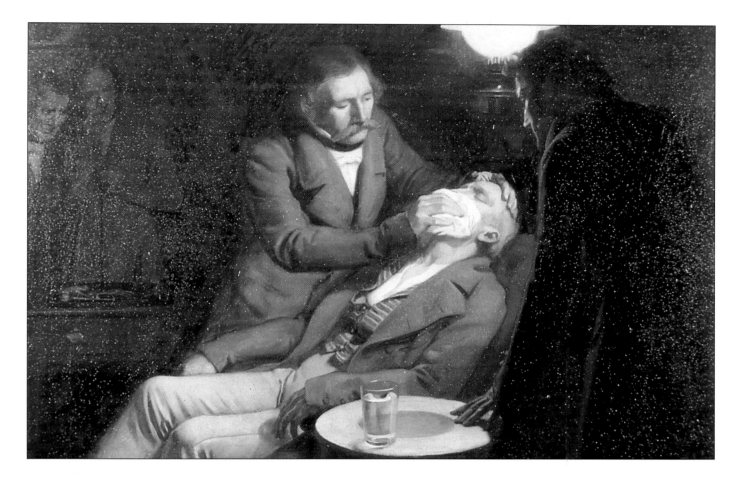

Ether and chloroform were discovered at the same time, the former in the USA. This shows dentist William Thomas Green Morton using ether to extract a tooth painlessly from Eben H. Frost in Boston, Mass, in September 1847. Morton later became an anaesthetist.

Gas which could take away pain was first reported from the Pneumatic Institution in Bristol by the chemist and physicist Humphry Davy in 1794. He found that the pain from a headache and a wisdom tooth were diminished when he breathed in nitrous oxide, better known as laughing gas. He suggested that it could be used in operations, but no one paid any attention. Students indulged in laughing gas parties, and subsequently ether sniffing parties, discovering that ether took away pain as well.

Ether was first used for an operation by an American dentist, W. T. G. Morton, to take out an abscessed tooth in 1847. The name anaesthetic was given to the gases by Oliver Wendell Holmes, and was adopted. Later that year J. Y. Simpson used chloroform to ease a difficult childbirth in Britain. Chloroform became widely used as an anaesthetic.

Today, several different substances are used to anaesthetise a patient. Ether and chloroform are no longer used at all; the patient is kept anaesthetised by a combination of drugs injected into the bloodstream, and gas. Drugs which keep the muscles relaxed are also injected. The anaesthetist remains with the patient throughout the operation, monitoring the breathing, heart action and blood pressure as the surgeon works.

Antiseptics

Throughout human history, people have died from infection of their wounds rather than of the wounds themselves. The human skin is an efficient covering which prevents bacteria from getting into the body; when it is broken, by something as small as a cut or by a major wound, bacteria and viruses can infect the blood and cause illness.

Doctors and surgeons did not understand how the body became infected or how diseases spread. The invention of the microscope by Leeuwenhoek and the discovery in 1675 of one-celled animals invisible to the naked eye called attention to the existence of microscopic organisms. Then, in 1795, Alexander Gordon realized that unhygienic midwives carried infection from one childbirth to the next.

In 1864, Pasteur showed that microscopic organisms in the air made wine, beer and milk ferment. He continued his researches and discovered the causes of anthrax and cholera in chickens, and in 1882 began work on rabies. His work was read by Joseph Lister in London. Joseph Lister had used microscopes as a child, but he studied to become a surgeon, and was appointed Professor of Surgery at Glasgow in 1860. He realized that the micro-organisms in the air could cause infection in surgery.

Operations became safer when Lister discovered the value of cleanliness. He invented a device that sprayed the operation and the surgeons with dilute carbolic acid, an antiseptic. It's use is illustrated in this textbook on antiseptic surgery by Sir William Cheyne, published in 1882.

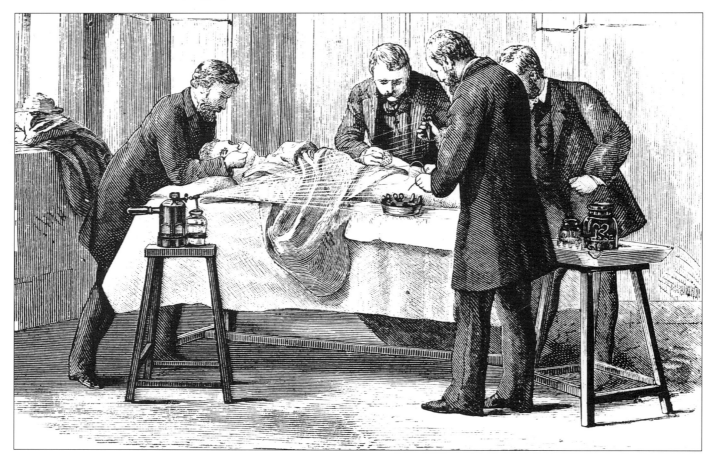

Lister knew that carbolic acid was a disinfectant, and he experimented by cleaning wounds with it. He found that it had to be diluted so that the acid did not burn the flesh, but that nine patients out of 11 were still alive with healed limbs six months after surgery. This was a much higher proportion of success than there had been in surgery without carbolic acid.

Lister used gauze dressings treated with carbolic acid on wounds, later changing to mercuric chloride and zinc-treated gauze. All his instruments and ligatures were disinfected, and the number of wounds that turned septic decreased. Other surgeons accepted his ideas, and the use of antiseptics became general practice.

There are many chemicals that prevent the growth of microscopic organisms, or even kill them. Surgical spirit, zinc sulphate lotion and potassium permanganate are very common antiseptics, and are now used in every household as well as in hospitals.

Above: Sir Joseph Lister was born in 1827 and trained as a surgeon. In 1865 his observations lead him to conclude that suppuration and wound infection were caused by something in the air. He read the works of Pasteur, which proved his theories and started antiseptic surgery. This portrait was painted about 1865. He died in 1912, having been knighted for his services to medicine.

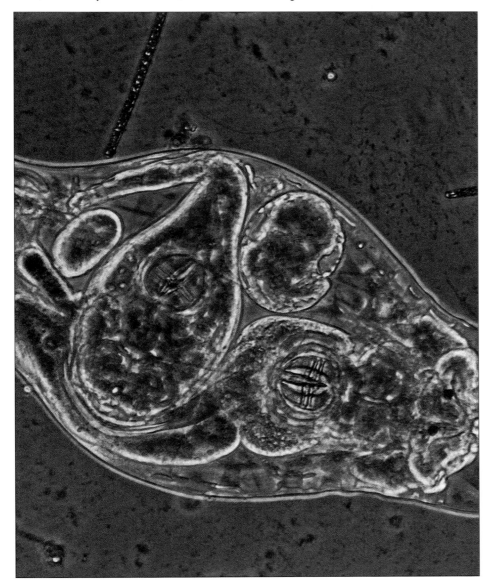

A bacterium viewed through an electron microscope. Not all bacteria are disease carriers, some are essential to life on the planet, but some are dangerous. They are easily transferred through the air because they are so small, but they can be destroyed by antiseptics and antibiotics. Bubonic plague, cholera, typhoid fever, diphtheria and food poisoning are just some of the ailments caused by bacteria.

Asepsis

Today, it is possible to perform operations in a completely clean atmosphere, with no microscopic organisms in the air, on the instruments or on the people in the operating theatre. Modern techniques make it possible to destroy any fungal spores, bacteria, viruses or any one-celled plants or animals likely to contaminate open wounds while the surgeon is at work.

The operating theatre is cleaned thoroughly with disinfectant every time it is used, and all the air going into it is filtered and cleaned; the fixed equipment is cleaned at the same time. All the surgical instruments are put into an autoclave, which sterilizes them using steam under pressure. The staff wear special clothing and footwear which is thoroughly sterilized, they wear masks over their faces and they scrub the exposed skin on their hands and arms.

Some patients have to be kept in aseptic conditions after their operation. There are sterile units kept free of micro-organisms by the same means used in the operating theatre. Visitors to these patients have to put on sterile overalls to cover their clothes and wear sterilized footwear. Babies are sometimes kept in sterile incubation units, and any nursing is done using special gloves in the side of the unit.

A premature baby being nursed in an incubator in aseptic conditions. The baby would have little resistance to infection, and the inside of the incubator is kept free of bacteria by the filtering of the air and by the use of built-in gloves to handle the child to avoid bacteria on the nurse's skin contaminating the air.

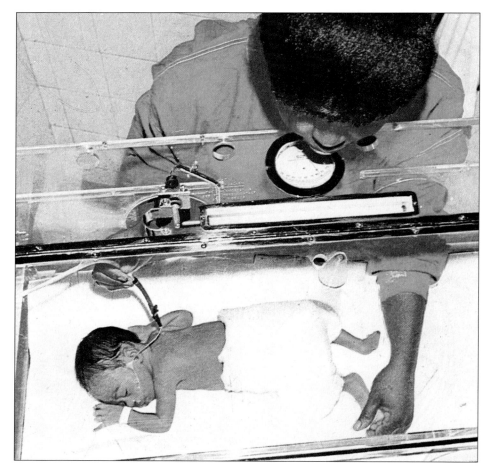

Modern Miracles

Surgery today is miraculous if compared with the operations of even 50 years ago. Surgeons can replace hearts, lungs, livers and kidneys, thanks to aseptic conditions and drugs that stop the body from rejecting the implanted organs; surgeons are able to break up gallstones and kidney stones without cutting the patient open to do so, they use miniature cameras to look inside peoples' intestines and can treat ulcers or remove tumours by remote control.

The transplant of human organs was made possible after surgeons discovered how to join blood vessels together. French surgeon Alexis Carrel was awarded the Nobel Prize in 1912 for his work on suturing blood vessels.

Once it was possible to give an organ a supply of blood, work on transplants could begin. After years of experiments the first successful kidney transplant was made in 1951 with a kidney donated by an identical twin. More research was needed to find a drug to stop the body from rejecting an organ from a donor who was not closely related. In the mid 1960s this became possible, and there are now people who have lived for 25 years with a transplanted kidney.

The pioneer work on kidney transplants opened the way to other

In the twentieth century machines have been invented to do the work of internal organs in the body. Dialysis machines remove the wastes normally removed by the kidneys. Below, a patient with diseased kidneys undergoes dialysis to clean waste products from her blood. She will be linked to the dialysis machine through canicula in her arm for some hours. Right and lower right shows a peritoneal dialysis machine, and a close-up of the drip into the patient's abdomen.

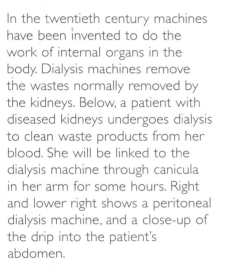

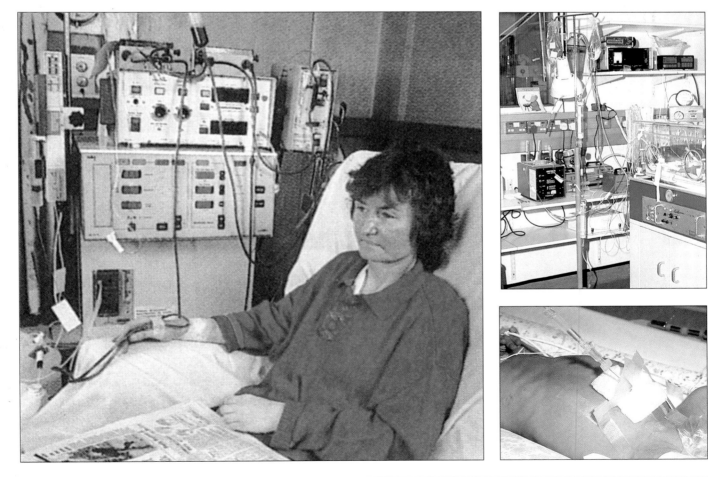

Open heart surgery has been made possible by having aseptic operating theatres and by the invention of a machine that pumps the blood round the body while the operation takes place on the heart. This picture shows an open heart with a valve being repaired by a surgeon. The repaired heart has to be strong enough to take over from the pump at the end of the operation.

organ transplants. The first heart transplant operation was performed by Dr Christiaan Barnard in 1967, followed by transplants of liver, lungs and pancreas. The longest-surviving patient with a heart transplant has lived for 20 years, liver transplant for 23 years, pancreas transplant for 10 years and heart and lung transplant for eight years. Transplant operations need suitable donors; in future, limb transplants may be possible.

If the possibility of new limbs, lungs or hearts is not miraculous, then operations by keyhole surgery certainly appear to be so; this type of surgery came about by a progression of ideas and new technologies.

One of the reasons that patients take a long time to recover from surgery is that their healthy skin, muscles, blood vessels and nerves have been cut or interfered with by the surgeon. The body of the patient suffers from trauma, or shock, on a grand scale, and this increases the recovery time.

Kidney stones, which are agonizingly painful, were traditionally removed by a major operation, traumatic to the patient, involving cutting through the skin and muscle, opening the kidney and removing the stone. But in 1979 the operation changed, and the surgeon removes the stone through a telescopic tube introduced

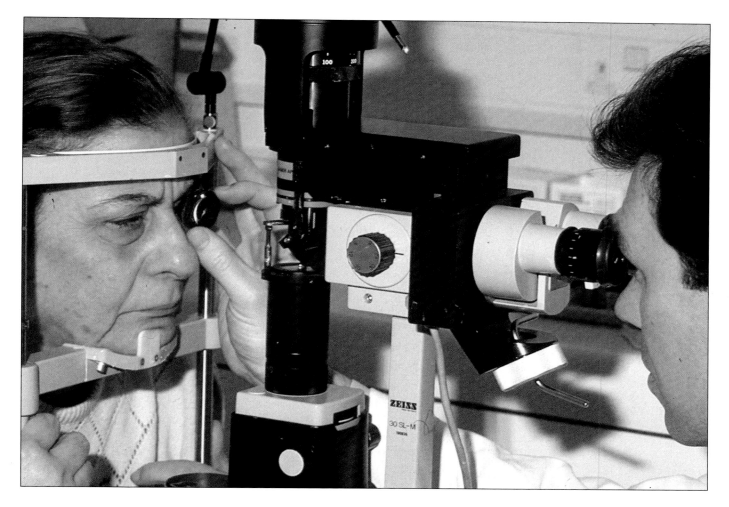

Another miraculous machine produces a laser beam. A laser beam is a directional, powerful beam of light, and it can be used to clear blood vessels, break up kidney stones and to do work inside the eye. Here a patient is receiving treatment for a damaged retina, the light-sensitive lining in the eye that helps us to see. This can be loosened by diabetes or by a blow and secured again by the use of a laser beam.

through a very small cut, just 1cm wide, straight down from the skin to the inside of the kidney. With the development of the technique of focusing a shockwave on to the stone and breaking it up, even the tiny cut into the body became unnecessary; the shockwave passes from outside the body through the skin and muscles into the kidney and broke the stone into fragments. No anaesthetic is required, nothing solid is put into the patient's body and the operation is no worse than a trip to the dentist. In the space of four years, getting rid of kidney stones changed from major surgery to a day trip to a clinic.

The rapid recovery of these patients led J. E. Wickham, Professor of Surgery in London, to propose a new kind of surgery in 1986. Officially this is 'minimum invasion' surgery, which means that the surgeon should cut into his patient as little as possible, to reduce trauma. This has been made possible by the invention of endoscopes. Endoscopes are flexible, transparent glass or plastic fibres that can carry light along them into the body and transmit a picture from one end, inside the body, back to a screen at the other end, outside the body. For the first time, surgeons could look into intestines, blood vessels, hearts, wombs or anywhere they wanted without making a single cut.

In addition, laser beams could be transmitted from outside the body to the inside, to break up blockages, cut out damaged tissues and tumours, and clear blood vessels without having anything exposed to danger from infection and without any major cuts into the patient. Mr Wickham called it minimal access surgery; when the press reported it they called it keyhole surgery.

More operations are being performed by keyhole surgery, which means that the patients do not have to stay in hospital for as long as they used to. Whereas patients once needed weeks for recovery, they now need only days, if that. Keyhole surgery could mark the beginning of the end for hospitals with wards full of beds for long-stay patients.

Not all the machines invented prove to be useful. Electric shocks were a fashionable cure for almost everything at one time. What these ladies are being treated for is a mystery, but it appears to involve both water and electricity. They look quite happy! Below, a patient in an intensive care unit surrounded by the technology that enables doctors to treat life threatening situations.

Miraculous Machinery

These amazing operations are made possible not only by the aseptic conditions, but by the medical machines that help to keep an eye on what is happening and those that can take the place of human organs.

Terrible accidents can be survived by the set of machines known as a life support system, which keep the heart beating and the lungs functioning when the brain is not working properly. These

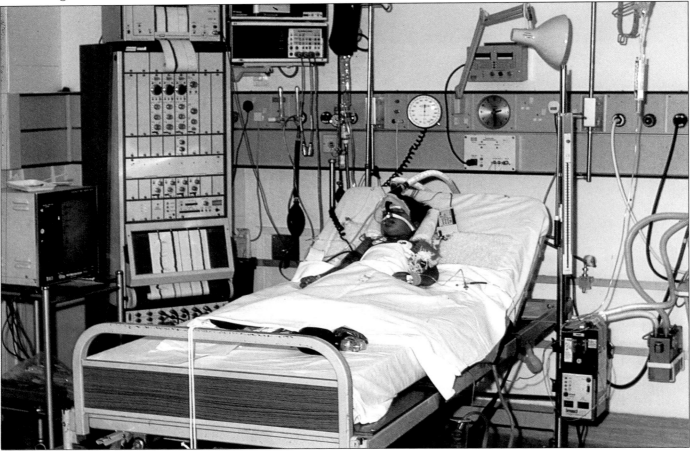

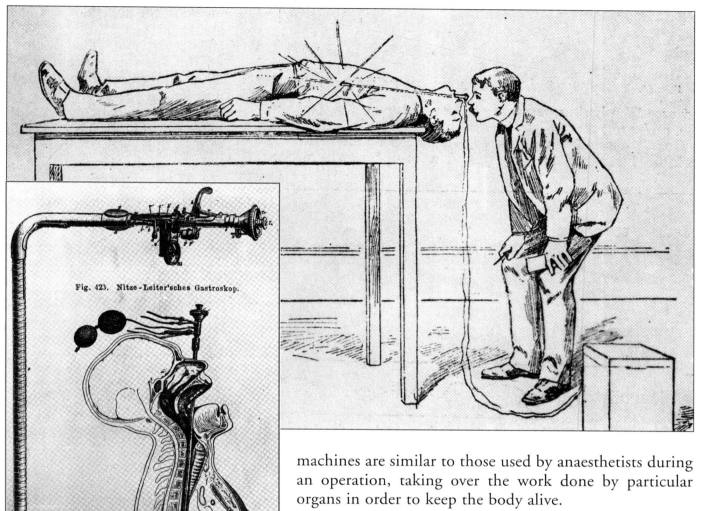

Fig. 423. Nitze-Leiter'sches Gastroskop.

The gastroscope was invented to look into the interior of the stomach, making it easy to diagnose ulcers and similar diseases. This early example is lighted directly by a battery-operated light bulb. Today, fibre optics make it possible to progress past the stomach and investigate the intestines and the gall bladder without surgery.

machines are similar to those used by anaesthetists during an operation, taking over the work done by particular organs in order to keep the body alive.

Heart transplants are possible because a pump outside the body takes over the work of the heart and moves the blood through the arteries and veins until the surgeon has finished the operation and the heart resumes its work. Renal dialysis machines do the work of the kidneys and clean the blood in the body. Those who are suffering from kidney failure can be kept alive by visits to a renal dialysis machine until a suitable donor kidney can be found for them.

A surgeon can find out what has gone wrong inside a body with the help of machines that can 'see' inside. X-ray machines show broken bones and shadowed lungs, but, linked with computers, a number of scanners can build up accurate pictures of working organs. CT (computerized tomography) scanners, ultrasound scanners and MRI (magnetic resonance imaging) are all used to investigate internal processes without any need for a surgeon's work. They can produce scans and videotapes of hearts beating, babies moving and any number of other functions. Modern surgeons and physicians have a magic eye that can look inside a body and show them what is going on, with no harm at all to the patient.

Chapter 4

REPAIRING THE MIND

It is only fairly recently that people have realized that illness is not simply in the body, and that it is possible to be mentally ill. Mentally ill or mentally retarded people have been viewed in many different ways through the centuries.

We simply do not know what happened to mentally ill people in prehistoric times. Mental illness does not leave marks on the body for archaeologists or palaeontologists to find. In primitive communities, madness is often regarded as holy, and perhaps prehistoric man saw it in the same way.

Because madness was believed to be the result of being touched by the gods or possession by a demon, it was thought not to be curable by doctors; madness was the concern of priests and holy men. This attitude did not change for a very long time. Even Hippocrates wrote about epilepsy as 'the sacred disease'. Romans and Greeks did recognize that some forms of madness were illnesses which could be treated, but this understanding was lost after the fall of the Roman Empire. Early Christians believed that madness was caused by possession by demons, and sufferers were exorcised to free them from the evil influence causing their condition.

Sometimes the sufferers were thought to be witches, and were persecuted or even killed for their illness; witches were certainly not looked after by their family and friends. The mentally retarded may well have been fed and kept clean by the family, and led a life in the community, but seriously disturbed people were likely to be locked up for most of their lives. Wealthy people could keep a sufferer incarcerated in one room in a house; many novels illustrate this, describing secret rooms and strong, silent servants. The monasteries and convents could provide shelter and care for poorer people, particularly as the belief that madness was a form of possession continued for so long.

In the sixteenth century, doctors began to realize that some mad people were actually ill. Several physicians wrote about melancholia. Thomas Bright published a *Treatise on melancholy* in 1586. Robert Burton published *The Anatomy of Melancholy* in 1621; in it he stated that tailors were melancholy because they sat cross-legged for long periods. He also believed that eating cabbage made people melancholy – many children would agree with him! Thomas Willis lectured on hysteria and melancholia in 1663 and Thomas Sydenham described hysteria and hypochondria.

Epilepsy was called the divine sickness because it was often suffered by very intelligent people. Both Alexander the Great and Julius Caesar were epileptics. When it was realized that mental illnesses could be treated, some of the treatments were very crude. This boy bears scars on his forehead from the attempts to alleviate his epilepsy.

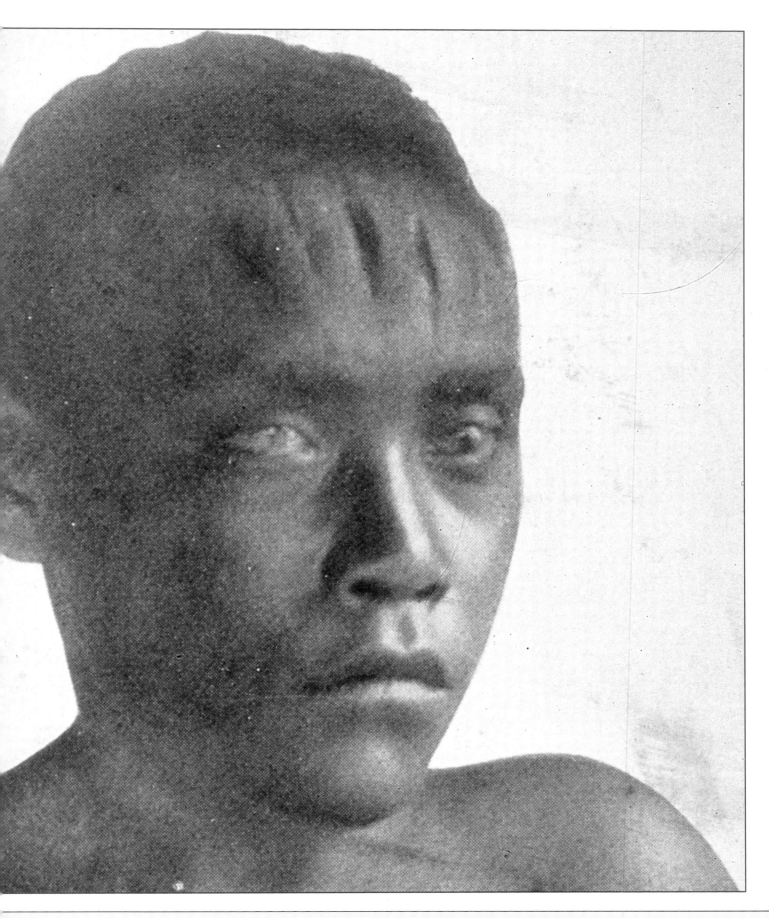

Mad-Houses

Because madness was not regarded as a medical matter, there were very few hospitals offering help and care for the mentally ill. If we follow the history of one of these it will demonstrate how care of the mentally ill changed through the centuries.

The Royal Bethlem Hospital in London was the archetypal mad-house. It began as a priory in 1247, attached to the church of St Mary of Bethlehem. The name changed to Bethlem, and in the fourteenth century it became a hospice for the care of wayfarers, travellers and the sick. In 1403 there were six mentally ill people there and in 1547 it became a royal foundation for the care of the mentally ill. The word 'bedlam' has passed into the English language and means an uproar or a mad-house.

The early history of Bethlem as a refuge for the mentally ill is a shameful one. The hospital moved from Bishopsgate to a new

Bethlem Hospital in the early eighteenth century, when it was fashionable to go and watch the inmates as an entertainment. This picture shows fashionable ladies and gentlemen strolling in the grounds, meeting their friends, visiting the caged patients and laughing at them.

building in the London Wall in 1676, and the patients were used as an entertainment for the citizens of London. It was at that time that the name changed to Bedlam. It was fashionable to go out to look at the inmates of Bedlam just as people would visit a theme park today. There was no understanding of the fact that these were patients; that they were actually ill.

This attitude was altered by changing medical opinions and by public opinion. The mental illness of King George III in 1788 generated interest among doctors and the general public. At about this time, a few psychiatric hospitals were founded with money from the public, and many small private retreats, called mad-houses, opened. Some of these were run by doctors, and others by untrained people; some were caring institutions, whilst a number were very inhumane and caused a few scandals.

The Royal Bethlem Hospital closed its doors to the public, moved to Southwark, and in 1815 was providing care for people who were then described as being 'criminal lunatics'. By 1863 it was realized that special accommodation was needed for the criminally insane, and they were moved from the Royal Bethlem to Broadmoor. The Royal Bethlem moved again in 1930 and amalgamated with the Maudsley Hospital in 1948 to become the Institute of Psychiatry, where research into the treatment of mental illness is carried out; a fitting end for a hospital with such a long association with mental illness.

King George III lived for 82 years and was a reigning king for 60 years, from 1760 until 1820. After 1788 his life alternated periods of hard, intelligent work with periods of insanity which increased as he grew older. He became irremediably mad in 1811. His son became Regent in 1812. George III died in 1820 a much beloved king, despite his madness, because he worked so hard for his people when he was sane. One modern theory is that the king suffered from porphyria, a disease caused by overproduction of porphyrins, which are produced in the process in the body that makes haemoglobin. One symptom is reddish-orange urine, which was recorded as one of George III's symptoms.

Asylums

By the beginning of the eighteenth century people were beginning to realize that madness was an illness which could be treated. It was still shameful to have a mentally ill person in the family, and there was a great worry about children inheriting mental illness , but at least there was some understanding that mental disorders could be cured. The new mental hospitals that were opened were known as lunatic asylums. Asylum actually means a safe place; criminals could seek asylum in religious houses in the Middle Ages, and could not be arrested for 40 days if they remained in a church. The name was intended to be a comfort, but in time it became a stigma.

Changing the public's attitude to mental illness took a long time. In 1793, French doctor Philippe Pinel began to improve conditions in the Bicêtre hospital in Paris where patients were chained to the walls; Pinel had them released and treated more gently. He made the observation that some of the behaviour of the inmates was as much a result of the way in which they were treated as of their madness.

In England, an untrained Quaker philanthropist founded a hospital called The Retreat, in York, which specialized in gentle, calm nursing with no extreme treatments. The patients there were kept peaceful until they were better. This was not the case in all the hospitals founded during this period: many of them used emetics, purges and blood-letting to quieten the patients.

Each county in England was empowered to provide an asylum for the mentally ill by an Act of Parliament, passed in 1808. The number of hospitals resulting from this Act provided adequate space and the patients were well treated. As more people moved from the country into towns, and as the population increased, people did not want to keep the mentally ill at home in the more crowded conditions, and more were sent to the asylums. These became very overcrowded, and conditions deteriorated, patients often being physically restrained so that they would cause less trouble. Doctors

The methods of restraining disturbed patients were crude and cruel. Two are shown here, a mask and manacles above and a strait-jacket combined with a barrel to prevent leg movement, all fastened to padding attached to the wall.

The horror of a ward in Bethlem Hospital about 1745, by which time it was named Bedlam because of the noise made by the distressed patients. Here an inmate is being roughly restrained for some kind of treatment – see the bowl in the foreground – possibly blood-letting to weaken and subdue the patient.

Charlesworth and Hill at the Lincoln asylum showed that these harsh methods were unhelpful, and conditions gradually began to improve.

There were no laws governing the admittance of patients into an asylum until late in the nineteenth century. Some patients were admitted to an asylum and kept there against their will. A law was made outlining the conditions under which an unwilling patient could be kept in a hospital; for example, when the patient had killed someone, an order from a magistrate was needed before anyone was committed to an asylum. This law was in force until 1930, when voluntary admissions were allowed, although dangerous people could still be committed by a magistrate without their consent. In 1959 the law was changed: instead of a magistrate, two doctors and a member of the family, or a social worker, could sign a commitment.

Psychiatry

Although it is not as ancient a science as that of the physician and the surgeon, psychiatry has become an important branch of medicine. Serious medical research into mental illness began early in the nineteenth century in France and Germany. Pinel published his *Traité de la Manie* in 1801 and J. C. A. Heinroth was appointed professor of 'mental therapy' in 1811; this was renamed 'psychiatry' in 1828. Mental illness was recognized as a serious medical subject rather than possession by demons, and research into treatments began.

Psychiatric studies originated in the German-speaking world, Germany, Austria and Switzerland. Mental illnesses were studied and classified by Emil Kraepelin; his categories are still used today. He recognized the disease that he called dementia praecox, which is now called schizophrenia, and manic depression; he also studied criminal psychiatry.

Psychoanalysis was developed by a doctor who had begun his work on nerves, but who is now better known as a psychiatrist, Sigmund Freud. Freud researched the causes of mental illness, and he thought that sexual influences in childhood were an important factor. Later researchers have shown that insanity can result from several different influences, and that heredity may also play a part, although heredity is not as important an influence as was once believed; Dr Morel, a Frenchman, thought that insanity grew stronger as it was passed on and his ideas made people believe that there was no cure.

With the rise of the Nazi movement in Germany in the 1930s, many psychiatrists left the country, taking their knowledge and experience to Britain and America. The psychoanalysts were among the emigrants, and in the United States, psychoanalysis became a popular treatment for mental disorders. Although psychoanalysts settled in Britain, the treatment has not enjoyed the same popularity.

Psychiatric researchers have discovered that mental disorders can be helped by hypnosis, drugs, electrical treatment and surgery. The attitude to insanity has changed; it is now regarded as a mental disease, just like a disease in another part of the body and, like most other diseases, it can be either controlled or cured.

Mentally disturbed people, with psychiatric and practical support, can now live in ordinary accommodation rather than in hospitals, and there are rehabilitation units, social workers, hostels and sheltered workshops to help them live as normal a life as possible.

Controlling Mental Disorders

The early ways of controlling people with mental disorders were just plain brutal. They were kept behind bars, like criminals, in the seventeenth and eighteenth centuries: some were put into manacles.

Opposite: Sigmund Freud was born in Austria in 1856 where he studied medicine and specialised in psychiatry. He became interested in language difficulties in 1891, but then turned his attention to psychoanalysis. He worked on human thoughts and behaviour and founded the International Psychoanalytical Association with a group including Jung and Adler. The Nazis labelled this as a Jewish doctrine and its members left Austria. Freud moved to London with his family but he died in 1939, soon after the move.

Below: A group of doctors hypnotise a woman patient. Hypnosis is used as a treatment for neuroses or hysteria. It can help a patient to remember events buried deep in their minds which are causing the problems. Hypnosis can also be used instead of an anaesthetic to allow an operation to take place.

The care was minimal, with straw on the floors and poor food. Conditions were often overcrowded, and the mentally handicapped would rub shoulders with the mentally disturbed and the criminal lunatics. No attempt was made to treat any of the disturbed patients.

Once mental disorders were recognized as treatable illnesses, conditions and treatment improved. Isolated hospitals were built, where patients could be kept in peaceful, quiet surroundings. The nursing staff and doctors lived on the premises, often in cottages that went with the job. There were male nurses as well as female, to help with violent patients; these patients were often put into padded cells so that they could not hurt themselves. These were still in use in the Second World War.

The discovery of drugs that could help to cure insanity was a real breakthrough. Syphilis, the disease resulting in general paralysis of the insane, was cured by penicillin. New drugs brought other disorders under control. Researchers found that illnesses responded to three different kinds of treatment, physical, psychological and social.

Most of the physical treatment today employs drugs. Anti-depressant and anti-psychotic drugs do not cure the patient, but they make life tolerable for them. The drugs suppress the worst symptoms, such as despair in depressed people, and keep the patients calm. There are other treatments, such as neurosurgery, which is rarely used today, when parts of the brain are operated upon, and electroconvulsive treatment, known as ECT, when electrical impulses are applied to the brain in order to lessen deep depression.

Psychological treatment includes counselling, when patients are encouraged to talk about their feelings, cognitive-behavioural therapy, in which patients are helped to conquer fears, and psychotherapy, when patients are helped to examine their past experiences. Psychoanalysis is a prolonged form of psychotherapy. Counselling can be undertaken by a doctor or a suitably trained lay person, but the other two therapies need a qualified clinical psychologist or a psychiatrist to see that the patient does not become too distressed and to be there to help if he does.

Some patients need only one of these treatments, but the best results come from using them in combination, with calming drugs helping disturbed people to talk about their problems without becoming too distraught.

Unhappily, many of the mental disorders cannot be cured, they can only be controlled. Schizophrenics and manic-depressives can live in the outside world quite safely provided that they keep taking the drugs which calm them and stop them doing foolish or dangerous things. If anything happens to disturb the pattern of their therapeutic drugs, their behaviour will become very unpredictable and they should quickly be taken to their doctor. He may well send them back to hospital to be stabilized again.

Chapter 5

CHANGING DISEASES

The diseases that humans have suffered have not always been the same. We do not know whether groups of prehistoric men were wiped out by swiftly spreading diseases, but quite probably they were. Certainly, diseases which kill large numbers of people have been recorded ever since humans could write. The great scourges of the world 3,000 years ago were leprosy and smallpox. There is a record of leprosy in India in about 1400 BC, and in Egypt in 1350 BC. Leprosy is mentioned in the book of Leviticus in the Old Testament, and in the New Testament in the book of Luke, who was a physician. Throughout the Middle Ages leprosy was an ever-present disease; sufferers wandered from one hospice to another, forbidden by law from entering towns. It was not until 1872 that the bacillus causing leprosy was discovered. In 1947 the British Leprosy Relief Association found that leprosy could be treated with dapsone, taken by mouth. Today, leprosy is an illness and not a worldwide fatal plague.

The fight against smallpox is a real success story. Smallpox was probably rife in 10,000 BC, and the mummy of Ramases V, Pharaoh in 1160 BC, shows pockmarks on his skin. Rhazes described it accurately in the tenth century and differentiated it from measles.

The Chinese inoculated against smallpox, using pus from a mild case and putting it into a scratch on a healthy person. Inoculation was used widely in Turkey in the early eighteenth century, and the wife of the British Ambassador, Lady Mary Wortley Montagu, took the idea back to Britain, and inoculation became fashionable! This worked well if the smallpox stayed as a mild strain, but it could kill the inoculated person if anything went wrong.

An English country doctor named Edward Jenner solved this problem in 1798. He found that milkmaids who had caught the mild cow-pox from their cattle did not get smallpox; if a person was injected with cow-pox, he would be mildly ill, but would not catch smallpox. Jenner called this treatment vaccination. People all over the world were vaccinated against smallpox and, in 1980, the World Health Organization was able to announce that from being a major killing disease as recently as 1967, smallpox had been completely eradicated in 1980.

A political cartoon showing Napoleon Bonaparte instructing the doctor to poison plague victims at Jaffain in 1799.

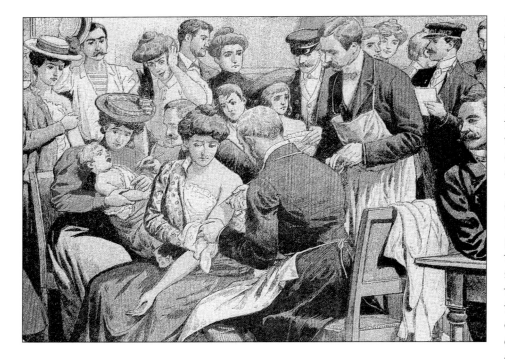

Smallpox was finally eradicated from the planet in 1980. This elimination was started by Dr Edward Jenner, who discovered that vaccination with the mild cowpox protected the patient from the dangerous smallpox. Mass vaccination, as in this Victorian clinic, reduced the danger of an epidemic in Britain.

Opposite: A classic image of a lone leper, ringing a bell to warn people of his presence so that they could get out of his way. The street is empty and the steps on the left crowded with the frightened public. Leprosy was once widespread, but is now confined to tropical regions. It is caused by a bacterium similar to the one that causes tuberculosis and it can now be cured with antibiotics.

Diseases caused by peoples' occupations have become more frequent since the spread of industrialization. Diseases of the lungs from work in the mines and work with asbestos, 'Phossy jaw' suffered by those who put the phosphorus heads on matches, and radiation diseases among hospital workers and radiographers are just a few of the new occupational hazards. Obesity caused by the rich diet of the western world and the diseases caused to the lungs and the circulatory system by smoking tobacco are modern plagues, killing large numbers of people every year. Stress is a new problem, caused by the hectic pace of life and the overcrowding in towns and cities. Humans no sooner conquer one disease than another appears to take its place.

Mass inoculation of the Burmese residents of Mandalay in the Bazaar by Dr Walter George Pridmore of the Indian Medical Service at the end of the nineteenth century.

People took strange precautions against catching the plague. The doctor in this fifteenth-century woodcut is holding a sponge soaked in aromatic vinegar to his nose to prevent him breathing in the foul breath of his patient. The doctors believed that the disease was carried on the breath. At that time it was unlikely that the doctor would wash his hands thoroughly or that the bedding used by the patient would be burnt, so the plague never really went away; the bacteria were dormant, ready to attack when conditions favoured their increase.

Great Plagues

When a disease spreads rapidly across a country or continent and kills large numbers of people, it is called a plague. Smallpox often reached plague proportions before vaccination was discovered. Queen Mary II of England died of smallpox in a devastating plague that swept across Europe in 1693 and 1694. Historian Thomas Macaulay wrote 'smallpox was always present, filling the churchyard with corpses, tormenting with constant fears all whom it had not yet stricken, leaving on those whose lives it spared the hideous traces of its power...Towards the end of the year 1694, this pestilence was more than usually severe. At length the infection spread to the palace, and reached the young and blooming Queen. She received the intimation of her danger with true

greatness of soul. She gave orders that every lady of her bedchamber, every maid of honour, nay, every menial servant, who had not had the small pox, should instantly leave Kensington House. She locked herself up during a short time in her closet, burned some papers, arranged others, and then calmly awaited her fate.' There was no help for the disease, the victim either survived with scars to prove it, or died. For centuries, smallpox never actually went away; it recurred and became progressively more lethal. Jenner's discovery of vaccination was the beginning of the end of smallpox in the world.

The Black Death, otherwise known as bubonic plague or 'the pestilence', was the worst plague ever recorded, killing 75 million people between 1347 and 1351. Ports began to quarantine ships coming from plague areas, making them wait for 40 days before disembarking. This explains the word 'quarantine'; *quarante* is French for forty.

In fact, it was the black rats on the ships which carried the plague-carrying fleas ashore. Humans caught the disease when they were bitten by a rat flea, and they would then spread it in the coughs and sneezes caused by the disease. The victim would be feverish and the lymph glands under the arms, in the groin and along the jaw line would swell. Towards the end of the course of the disease, these would burst, releasing dark blood – hence the name Black Death.

Bubonic plague is caused by a bacterium, and usually infects rats. When the rat fleas bite the rats, they became contaminated. The plague is still prevalent in South-East Asia, but it will never be a major problem again, as antibiotics destroy the bacterium, provided they are taken as soon as the symptoms are recognized.

Cholera was another disease which swept round the world, killing large numbers of people. It was a disease of towns and cities, where people were crowded together and where public health was poor. Cholera is still a danger today in Latin America and Asia, and also in refugee camps, where large numbers of people gather together in areas

Citizens of London fleeing from the Great Plague of 1665, when a large proportion of the population died. Mass graves were dug outside the city walls to cope with the high mortality rate and hand carts went round the streets to collect the bodies, the men crying 'Bring out your dead!' The Great Fire of London in 1666 had the advantage of killing off any remaining bacteria.

The fleeing Londoners carried the plague with them. They could have been burnt as plague-spreaders, as were these unfortunates in an old woodcut illustration. Panic caused violent reactions to a suggestion of illness.

Doctors believed that they would not catch diseases if they covered themselves completely. The curious beak is packed with aromatic herbs to absorb, as they believed, the bad air carrying disease. The mask and gloves protect the skin of the face and hands and the long robe keeps the bad air away from their clothes.

with no proper sanitary systems. It is purely a human disease, no animals are involved in its spread, and many humans carry the bacterium inside their intestines. Some doctors offer immunization against the disease, but it is not actually very effective. Personal hygiene is a better protection.

Cholera was first studied in 1627 by a Dutchman, J. Bontius, in the Dutch East Indies. He described the disease in 1642, and at that time it was confined to the East. There was an outbreak of cholera in China in 1669 and it spread to the towns and cities of the western world throughout the seventeenth and eighteenth centuries. Cholera found ideal conditions for a plague in the industrial towns of Europe in the early nineteenth century, and there was a plague, or pandemic, across Europe in the 1830s. Cholera killed 21,000 people in Britain during 1831/32, returning again in 1849/50 to kill over 50,000.

It was an English doctor, John Snow, who discovered how cholera was spread. Dr Snow was Queen Victoria's physician, but he also worked in Soho, in London, and when there was an outbreak of cholera there in 1854, he marked the cases on a map of the area. He discovered that they were centred around the Broad Street pump. People drawing water from that pump caught cholera: those using a different pump did not. Workmen in the local brewery, who rarely drank water, did not catch cholera, or had only a mild case. John Snow decided that it was the water from the Broad Street pump that was causing cholera. He talked to the Board of Guardians of St James Parish, who removed the pump handle. The epidemic stopped spreading, and there were no more new cases. John Snow had discovered how cholera was spread: in contaminated drinking water.

By that time, governments realized that towns and cities had to be kept clean, and sewage systems were built and care was taken to provide clean drinking water in cities. The bacterium that caused the disease, *Vibrio cholerae*, was identified. Cholera was under control, if not cured.

Not all plagues, or pandemics, are under control. A new one has appeared on the planet in this century; the as-yet incurable AIDS. AIDS is caused by a virus, and antibiotics cannot kill or even damage viruses. Scientists are working to find out what will destroy the virus, or at least slow down the spread of this disease.

AIDS is short for Acquired Immune Deficiency Syndrome. It is caused by the HIV virus, which lives in the blood and body fluids of those who have the disease. The virus destroys the body's natural defence system, getting rid of the antibodies that fight disease. Once the virus is active, it does not cause a disease and kill the infected person itself, but prevents the body from killing the bacteria and viruses that invade it all the time. As the virus destroys the body's defences, sufferers who catch any ailment cannot fight it; they may be lucky and destroy with drugs whatever they have caught, but sooner or later they will contract something that no drugs can destroy.

The HIV virus can be passed on during sexual intercourse, through blood transfusions or blood transference from one open wound to another. This last way includes blood passed on when drug addicts share hypodermic needles; this is a particularly likely way to contract the disease, and many HIV positive sufferers are drug addicts. Women with HIV who become pregnant will almost certainly pass it on to their babies. Doctors, dentists and paramedics who regularly deal with open, bleeding wounds now wear gloves to make sure that no blood enters any wound on their hands. People who indulge in casual sexual encounters should wear condoms to prevent infected body fluids from entering their bloodstream.

AIDS began in Central Africa which, with North and South America and western Europe, is where there are most cases today, although AIDS has recently spread to Asia. It was first recognized in 1981 in New York and Los Angeles, where it is more common in homosexual men. In Africa, it is more common among heterosexuals; it is here that the children suffer, being born with the disease.

AIDS is now one of the major causes of death in adults under 45 and in children under 5, according to World Health Organization statistics. The WHO has estimated that 5-10 million people are infected with HIV, and the number of cases is increasing rapidly. In the USA, one million people are HIV positive and there are 250,000 cases of AIDS. The disease is spreading all over the world, despite the money spent on advising people how to avoid catching it. It is truly one of the great plagues.

Malaria is still one of the outstanding problems of modern medicine. It is caused by a protozoan, Plasmodium, which is carried by females of several species of mosquito. It still causes high mortality in tropical Africa, Asia and Central and South America. The best defence is not to be bitten by a mosquito, as this army warning suggests, although the use of tobacco as a prevention can bring its own problems. Malaria can be treated by drugs in developed countries, and draining of stagnant water prevents the breeding of mosquitoes.

Chapter 6

THE WOMAN'S TOUCH

Woman's place in healing has been somewhat varied, because many of the world's religions to not approve of women as doctors, and sometimes not even as nurses. In the past, women were not supposed to learn to read or write, but it was natural for mothers to look after members of their families who were ill. It was also natural for women to be midwives – after all, many of them had experienced childbirth themselves. So, although they were not always allowed to study and pass examinations to give them qualifications, women usually played a major part in any healing arts.

There was no prejudice against women healers in early times. Asklepios had daughters who played an active part in healing; their memorials are in their names. Hygeia gave us the word for cleanliness (hygiene) and Panacea gave us the name for a universal medicine (a panacea).

The Arab world did not exclude women from qualifying as doctors; women trained in the Arab teaching centres, and in Salerno, set up along the lines of the Arab medical schools.

In Britain, the Law of Edgar, passed in the tenth century, gave women equal status with men and allowed them to qualify as doctors. They were allowed to train up until the fifteenth century, when the Guild of Surgeons put pressure on parliament and succeeded in having the Law of Edgar repealed. It was replaced by a new law stating that only men who studied at a university could practise as doctors. The prejudice against educating women was beginning.

Of the two main branches of medicine, women tended to be nurses and physicians rather than surgeons. In Europe, surgeons developed from barbers and tooth-pullers, both male occupations, and it was on the battlefield – another naturally male stronghold – that the art of surgery expanded. Women were associated with the mixing of soothing herbs.

In countries that followed the feudal system, the people living on a lord's manor would turn to his lady for medical help. Any good housewife had her own remedies for coughs and colds, to cool fevers and to help patients sleep; for hundreds of years the lady of the house

Traditionally women have always administered to their children; nursing is part of being a mother, so, inevitably, they have been concerned with medicine whether trained, like this nurse, or untrained.

This fifteenth-century surgeon is instructing a woman in obstetric techniques. He is telling her to wrap her hands in cloths soaked in olive oil before examining a pregnant woman. Women have always been involved in the practical side of childbirth.

looked after the health of her own household and that of the serfs and freemen who lived within the manor. Manor houses had herb gardens to supply the ingredients needed for remedies.

It was women living in towns who had a difficult life. Doctors were only for the wealthy, and, as more people moved away from their village communities into towns, the wise women who could prescribe herbal remedies and help with childbirth were scarce. Apothecaries, who could be women, would replace them, but even they cost too much for the very poor.

Women were kept away from education and could not qualify to become doctors again until the nineteenth century. Even then they had to battle to be allowed into universities to study medicine. The prejudice lasted into the twentieth century; at the end of the 1990s, even less than 20 per cent of doctors are women.

Early Herb Gatherers

In the Stone Age, when humans lived in wandering tribes, it was the women's job to gather roots, leaves and fruits for food. The women knew about plants, and they knew which plants were good for curing wounds or illnesses. So it would have been the women who steeped willow bark in water to make a pain-killer, dried and ground-up valerian roots to make a sedative, or used marigold petals soaked in oil to soothe healing wounds.

These early humans must have had amazing memories, because the knowledge spread as time passed, and it was not written down. The herb gatherers and remedy makers must have remembered all the medicinal herbs, how to recognize them and what they cured, as well as how to make the potions and salves.

The wealth of medicines stored in plants is enormous. One of the reasons that scientists and conservationists are so worried about the loss of the tropical rain forests is that plants that can potentially cure diseases may well be lost forever before the world can discover them and use them. The herb gatherers of the South American Indian tribes know of medicinal plants which today's pharmacists and pharmaceutical chemists would like to investigate, but the plants are vanishing with the rain forests and the knowledge of their uses will die with the Indian medicine men.

The Arab medical practitioners had a great knowledge of herbs, and women were allowed to practise medicine in the Arab world. These women would have known of the herbal remedies recorded by Rhazes. Here is a medicine intended to help an inflamed liver:

Take of red roses, ground fine, 10 drachms
Tabasheer, 20 drachms
Sumach
Broad leaves Dach seed
Lentiles peeled
Barberries
Purslain seed
White lettuce seed, each of 5 drachms
White Sanders, 2½ drachms
Common Camphor, 1 drachm
'*Let the patient take 3 drachms of this powder every morning in an ounce of the inspissated acid juice of citrons, ...or the inspissated juice of pomegranates, or the juice of unripe grapes and the like....*'

Inspissated means thickened or reduced by boiling. Pomegranate juice was used a great deal in Arab medicines.

In the Middle Ages the lady of the manor would not go out and collect her herbs from the countryside, she would grow what she wanted in the garden. Apart from the familiar mints, thyme, parsley, sage, marjoram and bay, she would grow hyssop, marigolds, chervil, mugwort, and perhaps the white eastern poppy, to make a pain-killing drink. Many different teas were made to soothe coughs, help sleep and to wash wounds.

Wise Women

Wise women continued through the centuries doing their work in the same way, with no formal training but an enormous amount of practical knowledge. Their traditions continued from prehistoric women, through all the disciplines of the Arab, Indian, Greek and

Women progressed naturally from herb gatherers and housewives with a knowledge of herbs to becoming apothecaries. This etching shows a female apothecary mixing up a potion for a child.

Roman civilizations, through the Dark Ages, the Middle Ages and the Renaissance until the eighteenth and nineteenth centuries. Throughout this time they preserved their knowledge of herbs and of childbirth.

They were there to help the people who could not afford the fees of the trained physicians and, in many cases, they were probably better healers than the theoreticians who worked from books rather than with people. Today their herbal knowledge is found in alternative medicines; the wise women themselves have been overtaken by education and urbanization. In the towns, the wise woman tradition was handed on to apothecaries. The Society of Apothecaries accepted women into its ranks, acknowledging their stored experience of herbal remedies.

Wise women usually lived in villages or small communities, where their cottage gardens supplied some of their herbs; the surrounding countryside supplied the rest. As they were not educated, they could not read or write, and their cures have survived by the same method as that used by prehistoric gatherers, by word of mouth. For example, here is a traditional blood cleanser:

Take the young leaves of dandelions in the spring and either chop them fine and mix with salad, to be eaten fresh, or press the juice from them and drink it.

and here is a cure for colds and hangovers:

Pick blackberries and weigh them. For every pound of fruit take one pint of malt vinegar, put both in a bowl and let them steep for seven days, stirring daily. Then strain and measure the liquid. For every pint of liquid take one pound of sugar. Add to the liquid, boil and allow to cool. Bottle it. If someone has a cold, put into a cup and add water. Give it to them to drink whenever they are thirsty.

It cleans up a morning-after-the-night-before tongue and supplies vitamin C too!

Not all the wise women were secular; some of them were nuns or lay sisters in a convent. In the early Christian church there were deaconesses, whose job was to visit the sick at home and look after those in the infirmaries. Many of these women were educated and were able to read and write. They probably would have kept records of their herbal cures and handed them on to their successors.

All these untrained but knowledgeable women were disliked by most of their male contemporaries. The physicians kept up their antipathy to women in medicine until the present century. A Belgian doctor, Johann Wier, wrote about women in 1563 saying that they were 'ignorant, wicked and boast of medical knowledge that they do not have. They tell lies to the common people who come to them for advice about all sorts of medical problems. They are not ashamed to say that the illness was caused by witchcraft and spells. It is these women who come from the devil.'

Witches

As the previous quotation shows, it was not difficult to gain a reputation as a witch. The line between being a wise woman who healed with the help of a knowledge of herbal cures, and a witch, who caused disease by casting a spell and cured with the help of the devil, was a fine one. It was only too likely that a wise woman would have a pet cat, which could be interpreted as being her familiar, an essential part of her spells. A vindictive neighbour, or an accusation from a jealous doctor like that by Johann Wier, and the wise woman would be on trial as a witch. When a person or an animal fell ill, the first thought was that it had been caused by a spell. Witches have been burned for causing cows to lose their milk or for horses going lame as well as for an outbreak of disease among humans, particularly in small villages where a household was likely to own only one cow or horse. Damage to such precious belongings was cruelly punished. Not that witches were always women, or regarded as evil; Robert Burton wrote in 1621: 'Sorcerers are common: cunning men, wizards, white witches they call them, in every village. They will help almost any infirmity of body and mind. We see commonly the toothache, gout, falling sickness, biting of a mad dog, and many such maladies, cured by spells, words and charms.'

In some parts of the world today a person can die if they believe that a death spell has been put on them. Whoever casts the spell makes sure that the victim knows that a spell has been cast. After that it is the person's imagination that convinces them that they will die, and they often do.

Women who were accused of being witches were put to horrible tests. The ducking stool was one of the worst. A witch was tied to a seat fastened on to a beam which stretched over a pool. She was lowered into the water and left there for a while. If she drowned, then she had no special powers and was not a witch; if she did not drown then she must have special powers and so she would be burnt as a witch. Whatever the result, once the woman had been accused, she had little chance of survival. There were other tests involving holding heated irons. Blisters absolved the woman of witchcraft; if her hand did not blister, she was a witch.

Once the true causes of disease had been discovered, witches became less credible, but belief in them did not die out, and there are still people today who call themselves witches. They follow ceremonies described in ancient books, but few people would expect to die from spells cast upon them. The last witch in England was burnt in 1712; the last in Scotland in 1722. The Witchcraft Act was not repealed in Ireland until 1821.

Witches made the news in the seventeenth century as thieves and murderers do today, although it was by word of mouth or by book in those days.

CHAP. L
Tue Tryal of Julian Cox.

*J*Ulian Cox, Aged 70 Years, was Indicted at *Taunton* in *Somersetshire*, about summer Affizes 1663, before Judge *Archer* then Judge of Affize there, for Witchcraft; which fhe practifed upon a young *Maid*.

Secondly, Another Witnefs Swore, That as he paffed by *Cox's* Door, fhe was taking a Pipe of Tobacco upon the Threfhold of the Door, and invited him to come in and take a Pipe? which he did; and as he was taking, *Julian* faid to him, Neighbour, look

what a pretty Thing there is; He look'd down, and there was a monftrous great Toad betwixt his Legs, ftaring him in the Face:

Nuns and Nursing

Nuns were women who dedicated themselves to Christ and entered a convent, vowed to chastity and poverty for all their lives. The first nuns were Roman Catholics, and there are very few orders that are not Roman Catholic today. As Christians, nuns were sworn to look after the poor and the sick, and it was natural that many of them became nurses. Some of the orders to which the nuns belonged were nursing orders, many of which are still functioning.

In the early years, they worked in infirmaries attached to their convents. These infirmaries cared for anyone who needed nursing, including the mentally ill. They offered an invaluable service all over Europe; the sick people of Britain suffered when Henry VIII dissolved the monasteries and convents and destroyed the hospitals which served them. In France these hospitals were called 'hotel dieu'.

Today there are still hospitals and hospices run by nuns, and several orders which are dedicated to nursing; some of them have roots deep in the past. The Hospitallers Sisters of the Sacred Heart hark back to the orders of Knights Hospitallers, and today they run hospitals. There are two Augustinian orders, the Augustinian Sisters whose mother house is in Brussels, and the Augustinian Nursing Sisters of Jesus. The Daughters of the Cross and the Poor Servants of the Mother of God are also purely nursing orders. There are others, like the Sisters of Mercy, who combine teaching with nursing. Many of these nuns work abroad, combining missionary work with nursing and teaching.

Nuns were well taught. When Florence Nightingale was asked to go to the Crimea to look after wounded soldiers, she took 14 trained nurses and 24 nuns with her because there were more suitably trained nuns than there were nurses.

The First Nurses

Apart from the nuns, nurses were untrained before the late nineteenth century. Before the Industrial Revolution, most people were nursed at home. The lady of the manor might call to offer help and advice, and a wise woman might be consulted, but the day-to-day care and feeding of invalids fell on the women at home.

While people lived in village communities and had their family and neighbours to help them if they fell ill, home nursing worked very well. When people moved from their villages into towns, it was a different story. Women had to work to earn money and were often worn out by childbearing; they had no time, and often no energy after work to nurse the sick. With a high mortality rate in children and mothers, in insanitary surroundings caused by overcrowding and poor public health, someone had to help out with the nursing. Some

Opposite: This caricature shows the general opinion of nurses and midwives in the eighteenth and nineteenth centuries. They were usually regarded as slovenly, dishonest drunkards; only nuns were regarded as dedicated nurses.

of the women who did so were conscientious, hardworking, kind and as clean as they could be in the circumstances. But many of them were lazy, unkind, unhygienic, drunken and often stole from their patients, and they did little more than sit in the same room as their charges. They earned nursing a very bad reputation.

This image was changed completely, all over the world, by one determined woman, Florence Nightingale. She envisaged a body of dedicated single women, not unlike nuns, who would devote themselves to nursing the sick. She thought that nurses should give up their duties when they got married – there was no room for divided loyalties in her nursing service. She was a fluent, persuasive woman, very well educated and able to write clear letters and reports, and she managed to convince the government of the time that her dream could come true.

She began her campaign in 1844, when she was 24. She had already refused to marry some very eligible suitors, and then she horrified her family by wanting to be a nurse. It took her seven years to convince her father of her intentions and in 1851 she went to a small hospital run by a religious organization in Germany for her training. Thanks to her prolific letter writing and the saving of her letters by her family, there is plenty of information about Florence Nightingale's activities.

She returned to London in 1853, to become Matron of the sanatorium for Sick Governesses. She found a badly run nursing staff and set about training them as disciplined, dedicated nurses.

The Crimean War began in 1854, the first war to take place in the era of steamships and telegraphs. *The Times* newspaper despatched a correspondent to cover the war and he sent back a graphic description of Scutari Military Hospital, which was overcrowded, had blocked sewers, no blankets, no bandages and no trained nurses. Public pressure forced the government to do something about it.

A cabinet minister, Sydney Herbert, who was a friend of the Nightingales, asked Florence to go to the Scutari and reorganize it, which she did. She took trained nurses with her and, despite the opposition of the military doctors, she had the hospital hygienic, well run and successful before she left it. The death rate fell from over 40

Florence Nightingale was a well-brought-up Victorian girl from a wealthy family and refused to fit into the conventional mode of living of her contemporaries. She turned her back on the social life and almost single-handedly changed the nursing profession, seeking a place to train as a nurse and then introducing discipline and cleanliness to the profession.

per cent to just 2 per cent, and when she returned to England in 1856, the British public were so grateful that they raised £50,000 to found the Nightingale School of Nursing. Florence Nightingale travelled all over the world, taking her ideas about nursing with her, to found nursing schools and to change the image of nurses worldwide.

Nursing Today

Florence Nightingale's method of training nurses is still used in many countries today. It took a long time to free nurses of domestic work; they were expected to clean and wash patients, make beds and then clean lockers and floors. That was how they started as probationers. They moved up the grades as they passed examinations, and became state registered nurses. Some of them could become sisters taking charge of the wards: and a few reached the highest nursing position, that of matron of a hospital.

The nurse's role changed as more technology entered hospital life. Cleaning duties were undertaken by ward maids, and healthcare assistants took over the washing of patients and making of beds while the nurses trained in specialist areas. They could decide on a career

Thanks to Florence Nightingale, nurses today are well regarded, have excellent training facilities and play an important role in the curing of patients.

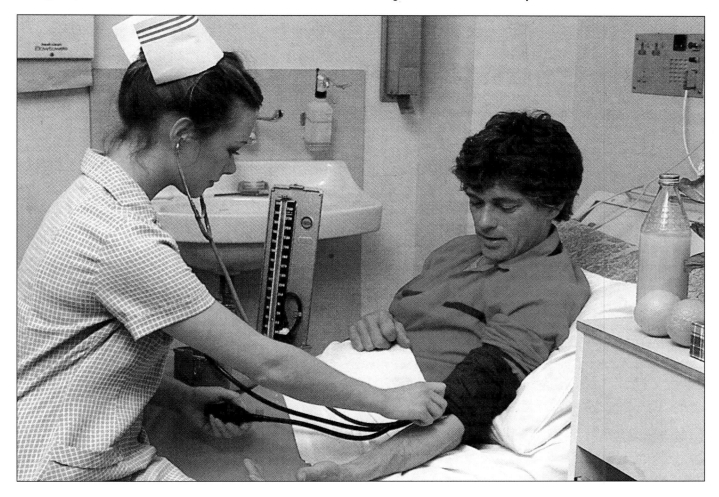

such as a hospital nurse, a military nurse, in occupational health, in the prison service, become an overseas nurse or work in the community. Community nursing includes district nursing, midwifery, working in family planning or entering the overseas service. Hospital nurses can choose psychiatric nursing, obstetrics, surgical nursing, nursing children (paediatric nursing) or nursing the elderly (geriatric nursing).

Nurses gradually assumed responsibility, giving injections, controlling drugs, and moving further away from pure care of patients towards a role that included a more active part in their treatment. As nurses take on more responsible work, so the standard of training increases. Nursing schools have combined with each other and with universities to offer degree courses in nursing.

The nursing services to the armed forces are trained in establishments attached to the navy, the army or the air force. The nurses have military ranks, and they go to battle zones to work. Historically, the armed services have always had medical support, and often by women. The Hadith, the Islamic Holy Book, says 'When the Holy Prophet (peace be on him) went forth to battle he was accompanied by his wife, Ummi Saleem and a company of women from among the Ansar who provided water and tended the wounded.' Men took over for a few centuries after that, until Florence Nightingale rekindled the woman's role in 1854.

Aboard ships, naval nursing was a job for well-regarded members of the crew called lob-lolly boys. Women took over as nurses in the Senior Service in 1884. Nurses were already an accepted part of service life when the air force was established. In the United States, an Army Nurse Corps was established in 1901 and the Navy Nurse Corps in 1908. The first female General in the American armed forces was Chief of the Army Nurse Corps, appointed in 1970.

Military nursing will probably combine with the non-military services in future, because as nursing becomes more complex to keep up with the high-tech age, the money available to the armed services is being reduced. Military nurses will probably join the civilian nurses in their university training.

Just as women are being accepted as doctors, men are now being accepted to train as nurses. In Britain, men were first accepted in 1947 as district nurses, and in 1960 the Royal College of Nursing changed its charter so that men could become members.

Lady Doctors

In the early centuries, there were women doctors practising in various parts of the world. Salerno had women professors, and throughout

Elizabeth Blackwell was the first non-cross dressing woman doctor in the world, but she had great difficulty in qualifying. She supported herself by teaching while she studied science to pass entrance examinations into a college. None would admit her at first. She was eventually admitted to the Geneva College of Medicine in New York and qualified as a doctor in 1849.

Europe there were women who could set bones, dress wounds and burns and, of course, make herbal medicines.

In the fifteenth century, women all over Europe were forced to cease practising as doctors by the medical guilds, and they were kept away from doctoring for the next 400 years or so. In Britain they were forbidden by a law passed in the reign of Henry V from even studying medicine, although they were expected to do most of the caring for patients at home. Men were so convinced that women could have no knowledge of scientific medicine that many of their undeniable skills, such as the preparation of herbal remedies, were deemed to be unscientific and unimportant.

This modern woman doctor may have had to work hard to gain her qualifications, but she did not have to overcome a wall of prejudice to become a doctor. Women today are readily accepted into the profession, although most become physicians rather than surgeons. Most surgery requires physical strength from the surgeon, and men are usually stronger than women.

Doctors in Britain had to be registered after the 1858 Medical Act, and there had to be a minimum standard of education before a doctor was included in the register. Women were not specifically excluded, but medical colleges and universities would not take them as students, and examiners refused to examine them. They could not gain the qualifications to become a doctor.

There was one woman who managed to get round this barrier of prejudice earlier in the nineteenth century. The determined Miranda Stewart Barry, born in 1797, dressed as a man and went to Edinburgh University as James Barrie and qualified as a doctor in 1812, aged 15. One year later, and still living as a man, she joined the British army and worked in a hospital. She went with the Duke of Wellington on his final campaign against Napoleon, and was promoted to assistant surgeon at the Battle of Waterloo in 1815.

Her career in the army was a distinguished one, and although her looks were rather feminine, she was renowned as a crack shot with a pistol, and for her quick temper. It was a brave man who challenged her! She became Inspector General of Hospitals in 1858 and died in 1865. It was at her death that it was discovered, to general amazement and shock, that Dr James Barrie was in fact a woman. She had practised as a doctor for 53 years, proving that it was quite possible for a woman to master the skills and knowledge required by a doctor.

The first woman to qualify without cross-dressing was an American, Elizabeth Blackwell. She was born in 1821 in Bristol, England, and moved to America in 1832 with her family, who were anti-slavery non conformists. She became a teacher, and saved enough money to follow her dream, which was to qualify as a doctor. She taught herself enough science to earn a place in a medical school, but the school refused to accept her. Eventually she applied to the Geneva College of Medicine in New York. The Dean said that he would admit her to study there if the male students agreed. They did, possibly as a joke, but she proved to be a good student and passed the examinations with top marks, to be awarded a degree in 1849.

During this time the townspeople refused to talk to her, so disgusted were they by a woman studying to be a doctor.

Dr Elizabeth Blackwell visited England in 1850 and went to Paris to study obstetrics in the same year. She returned to New York and opened a clinic for poor women and children in 1853. She came back to England, where she became the first woman on the Medical Register, and in 1874 she was appointed Professor of Gynaecology at the London School of Medicine for Women. She died in 1910, having inspired many women to become doctors both by her example and through the many articles written about her in the *English Women's Journal.*

The first British woman doctor was Elizabeth Garrett Anderson. She was born Elizabeth Garrett in 1836 into a wealthy businessman's family. When she was sent to an academy for the daughters of gentlemen in Blackheath, she met Emily Davies who was later to found Girton College, the Cambridge women's college. In 1859 Elizabeth Garrett and Emily Davies became involved in the Society for Promoting the Employment of Women and the *English Women's Journal*; a meeting with Dr Elizabeth Blackwell convinced Elizabeth Garrett to become a doctor herself. She became a student nurse and an unofficial medical student at the Middlesex Hospital, but was asked to leave.

She continued to study privately at St Andrew's and Edinburgh universities and, after a struggle, was licensed by the Society of Apothecaries. She had to threaten to sue them if they did not give her a licence, and they changed the rules immediately afterwards to discourage any more women from applying. Elizabeth Garrett, however, had her licence and was placed on the Medical Register in 1866.

She opened a dispensary for women and children in Marylebone, worked with the suffragettes and later went to Paris to study. She became a Doctor of Medicine there in 1870 and was appointed to the East London Hospital for Children that year. She married Mr J. Anderson in 1871 and had two daughters. She resigned from her hospital appointments, but continued her work to allow women to be educated and become doctors. She became Dean of the London School of Medicine for Women in 1883, staying there for 20 years. She died in 1917.

After the pioneer work by these two women, the prejudice against women becoming doctors began to break down. In 1865, Swiss universities accepted women, followed by Germany and France in 1869, by Sweden in 1870, the Netherlands in 1871 and St Petersburg, in Russia, in 1872. The London School of Medicine for Women was founded in 1874 by Sophia Jex-Blake, and universities began to accept women as medical students in many countries. It was not until 1947, however, that all UK medical schools accepted women.

Chapter 7

HAVING A BABY

Having a baby is one of the most natural things in the world. It is the way that each animal species ensures its survival. Reproduction is essential for the continuation of mankind, and if there had been any difficulty in the process, humans would have become extinct thousands of years ago. It is, however, a source of great wonder to those who do not understand the mechanism, and the connection between sexual activity and birth has not always been understood in primitive civilizations.

Humans do have one disadvantage when compared to the other mammals: they are walking upright in a body adapted to that posture from one designed to move on four legs. Being balanced on two legs puts a strain on backbones and hips basically arranged to have the support of four limbs, two at the front and two at the back. Being pregnant puts even more strain on backs, hips and legs and so human women can have problems.

Giving birth should not present any serious problems to a normal, healthy woman. Prehistoric women, who lived active lives and had strong bones and good muscles, probably simply stopped whatever they were doing, had their babies and then carried on, much as the other mammals do today. This still happens in some parts of the world. The western world has developed its own problems by adopting a way of life that produces unfit adults, often overweight and under-exercised. The recent past educated its women into thinking that having a baby was an illness, distorted their bodies by extreme fashions that made pregnancy difficult, and smothered the whole process with prudery and excessive modesty. In an era when table legs were covered and called limbs, because 'legs' was an improper word for a lady to use, it is hardly surprising that anything as basic as giving birth should be shrouded in taboos and circumlocutions.

Today, there is certainly no difficulty in talking about birth, and any problems are discussed freely. Women will visit doctors of either sex during their pregnancy with no embarrassment, and medical insurance companies make it quite clear that pregnancy and childbirth are not illnesses – they will not provide cover for the normal process. Doctors dealing with women and childbirth may be either obstetricians or gynaecologists: a gynaecologist deals with problems in a woman's reproductive system when she is not pregnant or is in early pregnancy (infertility would be dealt with by a gynaecologist); an obstetrician deals with pregnancy and birth.

All over the world, and in many different situations, women are having babies. In the developed world, most babies are born in hospitals today. In Britain in the 1920s hospitals were only used if some difficulty was anticipated; most babies were born at home. These babies being bathed at St Bartholomew's Hospital in London in the 1920s appear healthy enough!

A twelfth-century woodcut of the delivery of a baby by an Arab woman doctor. The mother has used a birthing chair, seen in the foreground, and is attended by a nurse as well as the doctor. Some things do not change; note the tub of water, and shears for cutting the umbilical cord.

Ancient History

The human attitude to childbirth has varied considerably through the centuries, from it being a natural process, through mystery and prudery back to acceptance of normality. Men were actually excluded from childbirth for long periods of time. Women in labour were attended by family and friends and the wise women or midwives were called in if they were needed.

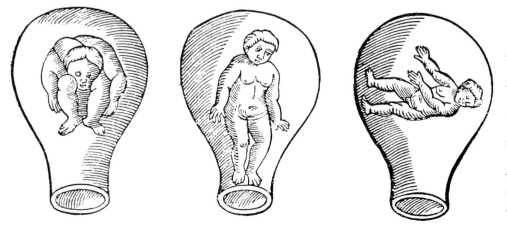

Doctors in the sixteenth century were aware of difficulties with the position of the foetus in the womb. This illustration appeared in a book published by Eucaire Roesslin in 1513. He practised obstetrics successfully in Worms and Frankfurt. His book was a great success and was translated into several languages, and was used until the end of the seventeenth century.

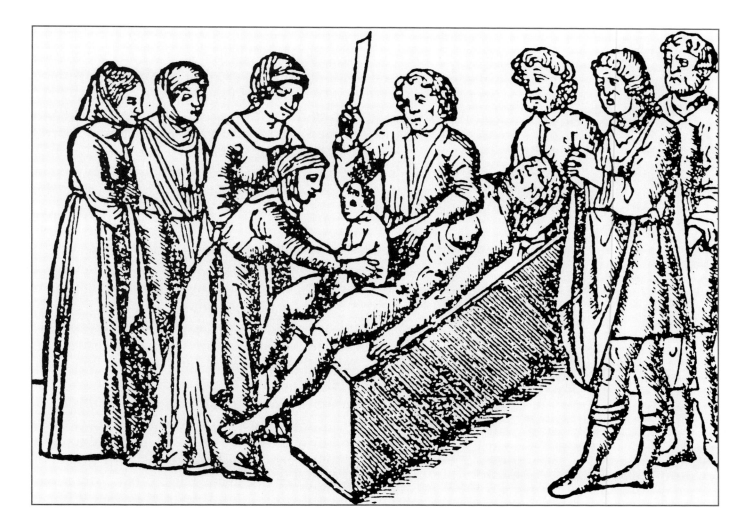

The Egyptian women sometimes had doctors to attend them; ancient papyri include sections on the diseases of women, the Kahun Papyrus saying: 'Knowledge of a woman whose back aches and the inside of her thighs are painful. Say to her it is the falling of the womb. Do thou for her thus; uah grains, sasha fruit 1 - 64, hekt, cow's milk 1 henu, cook, let it cool, make it into a gruel, drink four mornings.' There are Egyptian wall paintings of women attending a birth, so doctors were not always present.

In Greek and Roman times midwives were taught by doctors, and doctors dealt with any problems – the caesarean operation gets its name because it dates from a law of the ninth century BC, the Lex Caesarea, ruling that the foetus must be removed from a dead pregnant woman and buried separately. The Arabs had female doctors to attend them but, with the coming of Christianity, childbirth became the concern of midwives who learnt by apprenticeship rather than from training by doctors. The gap between the doctors in the universities and the midwives and wise women remained until the sixteenth century.

This woodcut is probably the earliest picture of a caesarean section, from an edition of *Suetonius*, published in Venice in 1510. The surgeon is a man, but all the attendants waiting to receive the child are women. The caesarean operation was already over 2,000 years old when this was published.

There were some very strange tales from that period. Paré, the French surgeon, turned his attention to obstetrics in his book on surgery. In it he records the birth of 35 live children to a woman in 1296. In time this grew to 365 offspring!

Paré wrote the first book on midwifery, published in 1513 in Germany, and he founded a school for midwives in Paris. Several books on obstetrics were published in the sixteenth century, when researchers began to investigate the foetus and comment on childbirth. The division between the people who performed the work and the surgeons and physicians began to narrow.

England benefited from the religious upheaval in sixteenth-century France; the Chamberlens, a family of French Huguenots, escaped to England and brought their obstetric forceps; (a family invention), with them.

Male midwives, called *accoucheurs*, became fashionable in France in the seventeenth century with Royal patronage. Louis XIV's mistress was attended by a surgeon, but most women were still attended by female midwives.

The doctors became steadily more involved in obstetrics during the eighteenth century; the first British school of midwifery opened in 1725 in London, and Edinburgh University appointed a professor of midwifery in 1726. Queen Charlotte's Maternity Hospital opened in London in 1739. Dr William Smellie published *The Theory and Practice of Midwifery* and was given the title of The Master of British Midwifery, although many midwives opposed his ideas. By the end of the eighteenth century *accoucheurs* were popular in England.

Ambroise Paré suspended his critical faculties at times. This picture of 'Dorothie, great with child with many children' appeared in his book *Surgery*. He recorded that she gave birth twice, the first time having nine children, the second eleven, and that 'she was so big, that she was forced to bear up her bellie, which laie upon her knees, with a broad and large scarf tied about her neck, as you may see by this figure'.

By 1595, when Mercurio published *La Comare*, the fashion in *accouchement* had changed. The mother no longer used a chair, as shown on page 102, but lay horizontally on cushions, with her legs down and her head lowered.

The birthing chair is in use again as seen in this Dutch woodcut from the works of Samuel Janson, published in 1681, but prudery dictated that the male doctor had to work blindly, a sheet preventing him from seeing his patient's body.

Below Left: Birthing chairs were in common use, probably because it was easier to work under a covering in them. Even the midwife has to work under cover in this picture; the excessive modesty extended to women at this period.

Below Right: The birth over, the mother rests on a bed while the midwife washes the baby. The cradle is ready at the bottom right of the picture.

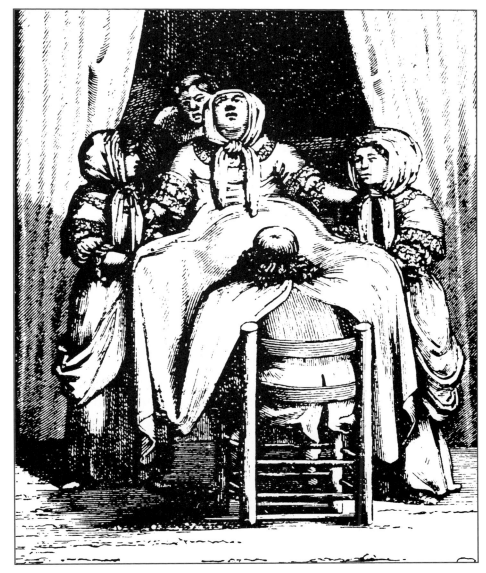

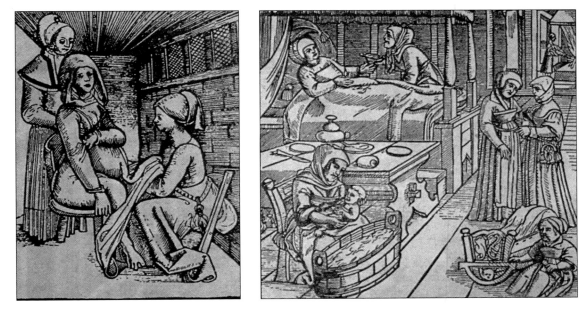

Population explosion

The changes caused by the Industrial Revolution took people away from villages into the towns. Diet suffered as a result; people could no longer grow their own vegetables, keep hens or catch rabbits for food. Overcrowding forced families to live in tenement houses with no proper sanitation. They no longer spent time out in fresh air and sunshine.

In these unhealthy conditions, rickets was a common disease, affecting bones and deforming skeletons. There was no birth control and the poorer women spent most of their lives pregnant. Labour was complicated by the effects of rickets and the lack of antiseptics meant that infection was all too frequent. The mortality rate in infants and mothers was very high. The highly contagious puerperal fever caused about half of the deaths; it was carried from one birth to another by the unhygienic midwives of the period. In 1861, Dr Semmelweiss, in Vienna, reduced the deaths from childbed fever simply by insisting that the midwives washed their hands.

The pain of childbirth was alleviated with the discovery of anaesthetics, chloroform first being used by James Young Simpson in 1847. The idea of making childbirth painless was resisted by both doctors and clergymen, until Queen Victoria requested chloroform at the birth of Prince Leopold. After that its use was generally accepted.

The idea that a woman could receive medical attention before the actual birth did not appear until 1901, when a bed in the Edinburgh Royal Infirmary was set aside for antenatal care. The idea spread; antenatal clinics were opened in Boston in 1911, and in Sydney in 1912. Even so, there was no decline in the maternal mortality rate (MMR, measuring the number of deaths per 1,000 births) in Britain until 1937. It is still very high in some developing countries, at around 500; this means that half of all mothers die in childbirth.

In the developed countries the mortality rate decreased when infection could be controlled with antibiotics, and haemorrhages could be treated with blood transfusions. Births no longer took place at home; there was an increasing tendency to have a baby in hospital, where modern treatments were more easily available than in the home.

Gynaecology started as a branch of surgery in the nineteenth century. Many of the operations were pioneered in America, where J. M. Sims operated to repair a bladder damaged during childbirth in the 1840s and opened the first gynaecological hospital in the world in New York. Repair to a prolapsed womb was carried out in 1888.

Improved diagnosis of pregnancy was not always welcome; the children were not always wanted. The subject of this watercolour of 1826 is timeless. The image of a baby in the urine sample in the doctor's hand, the crying daughter and the scolding mother indicate an unwanted pregnancy.

Having a Baby

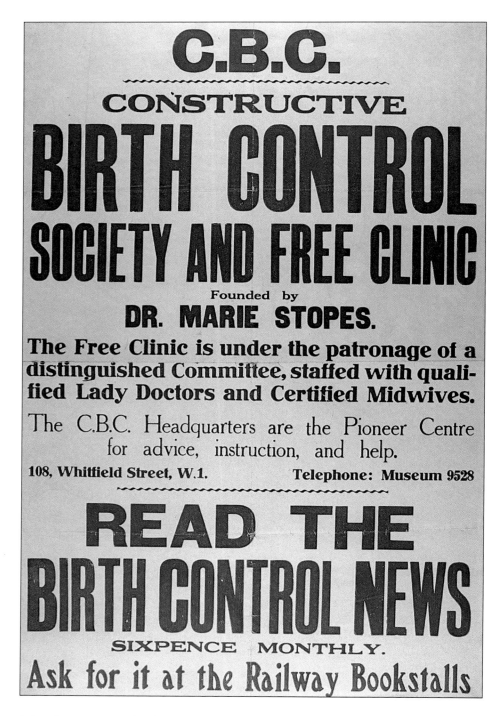

Marie Charlotte Carmichael Stopes, born in Britain in 1888, trained as a botanist, but turned her interest to birth control and contraception. She wrote *Married Love* in 1918, the book being translated into 13 languages. She opened the first contraceptive clinic in 1921 in Whitfield Street, London, making contraception available to poorer women and beginning the change in women's sexual habits that reached its peak in the 1960s with the introduction of the contraceptive pill. Marie Stopes clinics distributed the pills, but she died in 1958 and did not see the results of her pioneering work.

The first removal of an ovarian cyst took place as early as 1809, in an operation performed by E. McDowell of Kentucky. Lawson Tait carried out the first hysterectomy in 1874 and the first successful ectopic pregnancy operation in 1883. Oestrogen and progesterone were discovered in 1920, and further research developed the contraceptive pill in the 1950s.

Contraception dates back to the early civilizations, but it was not affordable to most women until the twentieth century. Spermicidal chemicals and physical barriers such as caps and coils were pioneered by Mrs Margaret Sanger in America and Marie Stopes in Britain. Clinics making contraceptive devices available to the general public were supported by local government, and the discovery of the contraceptive pill revolutionized women's sexual habits in the 1960s. By the 1980s, when AIDS made the permissive society a physical danger, condoms became readily available everywhere and were carried by women as well as by men. Advertising took away the furtive secrecy that once surrounded contraception.

Childbirth Today

Despite the ever-increasing world population, research continues to find ways of ensuring that more children are born. The pregnant woman in developed countries today has her pregnancy monitored at regular intervals with blood and urine tests and ultrasound scans to make sure that the foetus is growing properly. At the first sign of trouble, precautions are taken to protect both the mother and the child. If there is an incurable problem, the foetus can be aborted legally; the introduction of legal abortion in many parts of the world has reduced the number of deaths caused by back-street abortionists, and has improved the MMR.

When the time comes for delivery of the child, most mothers go into a labour ward in a hospital and the baby is delivered by a midwife, nurse or doctor. The pain can be controlled by a variety of analgesics, such as epidural analgesia, gas, or drugs such as pethedine. The mother lies on her back for the delivery.

However, more mothers are choosing to have their children using different methods; some revert to a practice used in Egyptian times, standing or using a birth stool to keep the mother upright, whilst others have their babies in a pool of warm water.

From time immemorial, there have been women who could not have children. Being barren was a curse in biblical times. Today, research has considerably reduced the instances of infertility. Semen analysis and ovulation tests and inspection of the Fallopian tubes all help to establish the reason for non-conception. Drugs can help ovulation and blocked tubes can be cleared surgically. Fertilization can be achieved outside the woman's body by in vitro fertilization (IVF) whereby an egg removed from the woman and sperm from the man are united and then replaced in the uterus.

Fertilized eggs can be stored, and replaced in the uterus at a later date. There are some women who bear children for another, either for financial reward or because they are family or friends. This practice can lead to difficulties after the birth, and there have been some acrimonious lawsuits in recent years because the surrogate mother has not wanted to give up the baby as she promised.

Sperm can be stored so that a woman can conceive a child after the death of her mate. Women married to men with dangerous occupations may keep semen so that they can have a child even if their husband dies.

While all these sophisticated techniques are used in developed countries, many of the undeveloped countries are still suffering from the diseases and conditions which developed countries overcame in the nineteenth century. The World Health Organization estimates that, throughout the world, one woman dies from pregnancy every minute, and it is hoping to reduce this figure by half by the year 2000.

Population control is becoming more important as the infant and maternal mortality rates fall. Family planning is an intrinsic part of gynaecology; in Britain the Royal College of Obstetricians and Gynaecologists founded a Faculty of Family Planning in 1993. Both men and women are choosing to be sterilized to remove the risk of pregnancy. There are about 90,000 vasectomies every year, with an equal number of women being sterilized. Hysterectomies are common operations for women who have damaged organs from past childbearing, and Hormone Replacement Therapy (HRT) is prescribed to ensure healthy bones and to relieve menopausal symptoms.

Children's Medicine

Human children are unusual among the mammals because they are dependent upon their parents for years, rather than for months, weeks or days as are the offspring of the rest of the order. They are helpless when born, take a year to learn to walk and two or three years before they can communicate verbally, and they need ten to twelve years to learn the basic skills of survival. Most do not have to go out hunting for food today, but the modern equivalent – the ability to earn a living – usually takes at least 16 years of learning to achieve.

While they are in this dependent state they are the responsibility of their parents, but today they are also the responsibility of the state. There is a branch of medicine specializing in their needs. Quite apart from emotional requirements during development, children are physically smaller than adults, so doctors and pharmacists have to assess the amounts of medicaments that their bodies can absorb safely. There are nutritionists to advise on the food, vitamins and minerals needed by a growing body and there are a battery of childish ailments to overcome *en route* to adulthood. Today, every effort is made by parents and the state to give a child a healthy start in life.

Paediatrics, the branch of medicine specializing in the ailments of children, is as old as medicine itself. The Egyptian papyri, Indian and

Chinese writings all leave records of children's diseases, of their symptoms and treatments. The lists are still familiar today; teething problems, measles, coughs, colds and sores were as common 3,000 years ago as they are today. In 1765, Professor Rosen von Rosenstein of Uppsala in Sweden wrote a book on children's diseases and their treatment; he established modern paediatrics.

The French government after the Revolution built an Hôpital des Enfants Malades in Paris in 1802, and funded research into children's illnesses. Private children's hospitals were opened in Berlin, St Petersburg and Vienna in the 1830s and The Hospital for Sick Children in Great Ormond Street, London, was opened by Charles West in 1852. All these hospitals were trying to reduce the very high death-rate of children in the industrial towns. They were not outstandingly successful in this, but they carried out valuable research into childhood illnesses.

The researchers quickly realized that the major problems were child labour, malnutrition and lack of hygiene. The children had little or no resistance to infectious diseases. Deaths from smallpox, tuberculosis, tetanus, diphtheria, whooping cough, scarlet fever and other common ills were frequent. Conditions were improved partly by anti-child labour campaigns begun in the nineteenth century, by improvements in public health and by information on nutrition, and by immunization against many common childhood ailments. Children were immunized from birth as safe doses of vaccine were developed. The long battle against smallpox was won early in the twentieth century when it became standard practice to vaccinate the very young.

The fight against tuberculosis, begun in 1882 when Dr Heinrich Koch identified the bacillus causing the disease and continued by an intensive treatment campaign, was finally won with the help of radiography and antibiotics.

Diphtheria was the first of the diseases to be overcome by an immunization programme. The problem of allergic reactions to the serum in which the vaccine was carried had to be overcome before the vaccine became generally used, but a vaccination programme began as clinical trials in the 1920s. By the 1940s, British children were automatically immunized at school despite some resistance from both parents and doctors. Diphtheria is no longer a common disease in Europe.

Poliomyelitis grew to epidemic proportions in 1910 and devastated the population of children until 1951, when it swept across America and Sweden. It was overcome by the Salk vaccine which was developed from 1953. Children can take this on a cube of sugar, ensuring escape from a disease that often left its survivors crippled.

Surprisingly, it was the Second World War that revolutionized diets in Britain. The isolation caused by the war and the problems of feeding the population resulted in food rationing. Every person had a nutritionally balanced ration of food. Children had extra milk and fruit juice to ensure that they had enough minerals and vitamins for growing; for the first time, many children had enough of the right food to eat. The health of the nation improved.

With the battle for healthy bodies won, new problems appeared. In animal populations, overcrowding results in fighting between the individuals in a community. Apparently the same is true in humans. As the world population rockets, and people live in increasingly crowded towns and cities, the incidence of child abuse is increasing. Paediatrics now has to deal with the mental problems arising from emotionally deprived childhood, cruelty and child abuse.

Children themselves have found new problems to overcome. Lack of exercise is one example. Children no longer play games after school; they go home to watch television or play computer games. Many of them rarely walk for more than ten minutes a day because they go to school in buses or cars, and many schools no longer include games in the syllabus. In the affluent countries, children have plenty of money and spend it on "junk" food, high in fats and sugar, and many children in developed countries are overweight and very unfit.

Gilray's etching of the vaccination clinic at St Pancras' Smallpox and Inoculation Hospital shows the campaign against smallpox in full swing. By the early 1900s it was standard practice to inoculate children against smallpox at a few weeks old. With immunization against diphtheria, the other great child-killer, the chances of surviving to adulthood increased considerably.

Chapter 8

SPELLS, SALVES AND SIMPLES

The link between medicine and magic has existed for thousands of years. The human mind is a powerful medicine in its own right, and cures can come about because someone has decided to get better. This may be called positive thinking, it may be faith-healing or it may, in some places, still be called witchcraft. The fact remains that some cures are very difficult to explain in purely scientific terms.

Modern doctors use this power of self-healing as much as witch-doctors. Sometimes they prescribe placebos, medicines that have no medical contents. Placebos are often used when new drugs are being investigated, to assess the mental lift experienced by the taker in the knowledge that he has taken a 'cure'. The kick-start that the dose gives to the brain sets the self-healing process in action, even though there is nothing in the dose other than everyday food. The curative property of a placebo is called the placebo effect, and is a valid treatment for some ills.

Although the body can cure itself, provided it does not have too much to combat, humans have helped with ointments, infusions, tinctures, simples, syrups, suppositories, pills and all kinds of modern aids such as injections; and most of the effective medicaments have originated in the plant world. Humans have explored the healing properties of herbs for thousands of years, and they are still discovering healing plants today. One of the concerns over the destruction of the rain forests is the loss of as-yet undiscovered healing drugs.

The humans who began to investigate the healing powers of plants were the wise women who gathered them in the Stone Age, followed by the medicine men, the witch-doctors and the Egyptian, Greek and Arab doctors. The people who specialized in making medicines in later centuries were the alchemists and apothecaries, who took over when the doctors became more concerned with the academic aspects of medicine.

The medicine show was not isolated to the USA. This cartoon shows an itinerant medicine vendor performing on stage with his two assistants before selling his universal remedy to the watching crowd in Georgian Britain.

The alchemists were actually more concerned with turning everything into gold and spent their time searching for the philosopher's stone, which was supposed to be able to turn everything to gold, but they did make some chemical discoveries in the course of their quest.

The apothecaries collected the information handed down via the

Flemish painter Pieter Bruegel the Elder was inspired to paint *The Goldmaker*, showing the interior of an alchemist's work-room in fascinating detail. The alchemist – on the left reads a formula from his book while his assistant on the

right mixes the ingredients to his instruction. Bruegel's eye for detail gives a wonderful picture of sixteenth-century life.

In this coloured etching of 1825 by Henry Heath entitled "Physic", the display of a typical pharmacy of the period is portrayed. The boy assistant is grinding ingredients with a pestle and mortar.

wise women, and preserved their knowledge. They made up a variety of medicines, some of which were not particularly useful, but many of which are the basis of the modern wound healers, cough soothers and fever reducers. Many of the apothecaries went out into the countryside, collected their own ingredients and made up the ointments and cough syrups themselves.

Herbal Knowledge

The ways of using herbs have not changed much for centuries. The most common method of preparing a liquid is to make an infusion. That is not as unfamiliar as it sounds: tea is an infusion. Infusions

are made by pouring 500ml of boiling water over two tablespoons of leaves, flowers or stems. The plants may be fresh or dried. Another method of preparing a liquid is to make a decoction: barks, roots, tough stems, seeds or wood chips are boiled for half an hour in water.

A tincture is a liquid made with alcohol, and takes longer to prepare. The herb is powdered or crushed and put into a glass jar with 30ml of alcohol and 10ml of distilled water. Put a tight lid on it and leave it in a warm place for about two weeks. Store in a cool dark place.

Poultices are solids, made by pounding leaves, flowers or stems to a paste in a mortar; the paste is wrapped in clean muslin and applied to a wound or bruise. Ointments were once made by pounding herbs into soft fat, such as goose grease, that had been cleaned by boiling in water, and which was scooped off the water when it had cooled. All these methods are centuries old.

The scientific names of plants give away their medicinal uses. Plants are identified by two names. The first, the *generic* name, is a kind of surname belonging to a group of plants. The second, the *specific* name, belongs to just one plant. If the specific name

With the discovery of the New World a flood of new medicinal herbs reached Europe. These examples of Mexican plants and animals were pictured in 1651 by Hernandez, physician to Philip II of Spain. He is fairly accurate. The hoatzin and iguana in the foreground are identifiable and the tree above the iguana could well be the ipecacuanha tree, used in cough mixture and as an emetic.

By 1696 the New World plants ipecacuanha and Virginian snake root are illustrated with rhubarb and other European medicinal herbs in Pomet's *Histoire Generale des Drogues*.

is *officinalis*, then it has been used as a medicinal herb in the past.

Many of the herbs used in remedies are still used in cooking. That familiar herb in stuffing, sage or *Salvia officinalis*, has medicinal uses. The Arab doctors asked 'How can a man die if he has sage in his garden?' Infusion of sage can be used as a remedy for colds and fevers, to ease rheumatism and to soothe coughs. It is also a disinfectant, and can be used as a gargle for a sore throat. Similarly, thyme or *Thymus vulgaris*, is used to help bronchitis, whooping cough or indeed any cough, and thyme oil is a pain-killer for toothache. It is also a sedative.

A more unlikely medicinal herb is the flower, Golden Rod or *Solidago virgaurea*. This was brought to Europe from the Middle East by the returning crusaders because it was a good wound healer. It was very expensive until people discovered that it grew very easily in Europe. A golden rod infusion can be used to clean a wound and an ointment or poultice may be put over it. More recently, drinking an infusion has helped sufferers with kidney and bladder stones.

Camomile, *Matricaria chamomilla*, is a strong sedative, drunk as an infusion, and will also help to heal sore mouths. Parsley helps to

Wm Edwards Del.   Pub by T. Curtis St Geo. Crescent Nov.r 11810.   E. Sansom Jun Sc.

Ginseng, *Panax pseudoginseng*, is one of the oldest of the medicinal herbs, used in Chinese medicine for centuries and fashionable as a tonic among those interested in complementary medicine today. There is a North American plant, *Panax quinquefolius*, which was exploited to near extinction in recent years by commercial tonic makers.

ease rheumatism, rosemary benefits blood circulation, valerian is a sedative, dandelion is a diuretic and an aid to digestion. All around us, plants that we look upon as weeds have valuable medical properties which most people know nothing about.

Power Plants

Apart from these everyday herbal remedies, there are more powerful ones. Many of the major poisons come from plants. The Deadly Nightshade, *Atropa belladonna*, gives atropine, a little of which is a valuable drug while a larger dose will kill. Small doses of strychnine are a tonic, while larger doses kill. This drug comes from a tropical tree, *Strychnos nux-vomica*. Many of the drugs which come from these powerful plants are medicinal in small doses and poisonous in larger doses.

One of the oldest of all drugs, opium, which comes from the white poppy *Papaver somniferum*, is as valuable a pain-killer and sleep inducer as morphine and codeine, but in larger quantities it is a dangerous addictive drug. It is also the source of heroin, which is so dangerously addictive that it is no longer prescribed by doctors in some countries.

Coca leaves, from the Peruvian shrub *Erythroxelon coca*, have been chewed by Peruvians for centuries. They stop the very poor from feeling hungry and help messengers to run long distances without pain. It is also the source of cocaine, extracted from the leaves and used as a powerful local anaesthetic by such people as dentists, and which is another of the addictive drugs.

The foxglove *Digitalis purpurea* gives us digitalis, the heart medicine. It was first formally described in 1776 by William Withering, who said in his paper *'An account of the foxglove'* that he had been told by an old wise woman that foxglove was good for dropsy. He extracted what he called digitalin from foxgloves in 1785,

Opium has been used as a medicine for over 2,000 years, but it is also proof that drug abuse is not a new phenomenon. Used by Chinese doctors to deaden pain, it was also smoked for its hallucinatory effects by some people. Opium addicts would lose interest in real life, neglecting to eat properly. This nineteenth-century engraving shows opium smokers in Malaya.

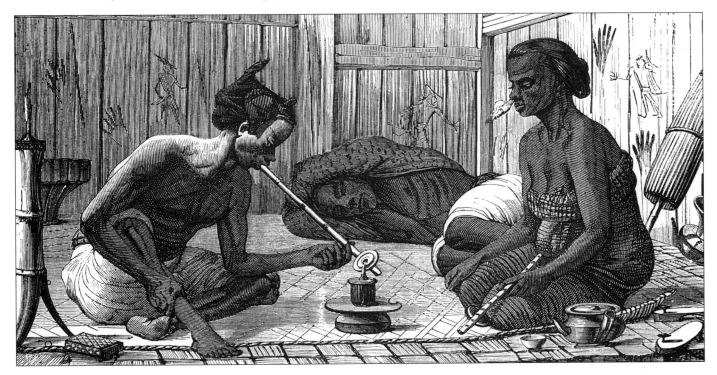

Cinchona bark from Peru was used to control fever in Italy in the sixteenth century when malaria was a common disease. Quinine from the bark is still used for the same purpose today. This fresco in the Santo Spirito Hospital in Rome shows the Countess of Chinchon receiving a cup of tincture of fever tree bark from her physician. A Peruvian Indian holding a bundle of the bark kneels at her feet.

ÆCROTAT LIMÆ CONIUX CHINCONIA FEBRIM CORTICE MIRANDO POCULA TINCTA FUGANT

A seventeenth-century bottle labelled Ess. Chin: Chin: used for cinchona preparation by a pharmacist in Mainz in Germany.

and it has been used ever since for regulating the heart and for treating heart attacks.

It was not until the twentieth century that the anti-bacterial properties of the fungi were discovered. In 1928, Alexander Fleming found that *Penicillium notatum* stopped bacteria growing and he isolated penicillin from the fungus, but it was not until the Second World War that it was developed for clinical use. Fleming, Howard Florey and Ernst Chaim were awarded the Nobel Prize for medicine in 1945 for the discovery and development of the antibiotic that has saved thousands of lives and played an important part in destroying some diseases. Since then *Streptomyces*, a genus of single-celled micro-organisms living in the soil, have given antibiotics such as streptomycins and tetracyclines.

These antibiotics attack bacteria, but do not touch viruses. Viruses are certainly inhibited by another plant, however. Garlic, long recommended to combat the common cold which is caused by a virus, contains interferon, which scientists have discovered will interfere with virus production in the cells of the body.

These are a very few of the drugs and antibiotics which come from the plant world. Some have been known for thousands of years, others have only just been discovered. The American Indians knew that a decoction of the bark of the cinchona reduced fevers, and we still use it as quinine. Prehistoric people probably knew that a decoction of willow bark helped fever and rheumatic pains; we use that as aspirin. The medicine men of South American Indian tribes

Sir Alexander Fleming (centre) discusses his research into the fungus *Penicillium* and the development of the drug penicillin with an Italian and a Russian colleague in Rome in 1945.

used the plants that gave us caffeine, ipecac, ephredine, and nicotine long before they entered pharmaceutical lists, and discoveries like the Rosy Periwinkle, *Vinca*, used by healers in Jamaica and Madagascar, are already helping to combat leukaemia and other cancers with vincristine and vinblastine.

There is a treasure-house of medicinal drugs still to be discovered among the tropical plants.

Alarming Remedies

Not all the remedies used in the past were useful and sensible; humans have tried some very strange cures. The animal kingdom does not produce the wealth of medicines found in the plant world, but humans have used parts of them, and in some places still do, for the characteristics shown by the animal. In extreme cases, cannibals eat brave opponents when they catch them to acquire their courage. In the same way, some animals are eaten to produce speed or strength. It rarely works!

One of the most famous of the medicines of the past was theriac,

which was certainly used from the eleventh century until the seventeenth century. It was made from a variety of plants, depending on the apothecary making it, but the most important ingredient was dried, powdered viper. The viper is one of the animals that does contribute to modern medicine; the venom is used to help haemophiliac blood to clot, but the venom is milked from the snake and the constituent that causes clotting is isolated from it. Drying the whole animal and powdering it would not have much effect!

Ioan. Stradanus. inuent.

Corn. Galle sculp.
Ioan Galle excud.

Above: The essential ingredient of theriac was powdered dried viper. There was a great trade in these snakes – the British adder being one of the genus – and money to be made supplying the apothecary with the snakes. This woodcut from about 1500 shows a viper collecting expedition in action.

Opposite Top: A fifteenth-century woodcut showing a man extracting a toad stone. Despite evidence to the contrary, the toad was believed to carry a stone in its head. If set in a ring touching the flesh the toad stone would become very hot in the presence of a poison, warning the wearer of poisoned food or drink – or so they thought in Shakespeare's time. The stone was believed to be an antidote to poison as well.

Opposite Below: A packet of theriac surviving from 1695 until today. There are many examples of containers for this medicine – bottles, jars and boxes, but this one still contained the actual substance.

An enterprising theriac vendor displays a viper to show that the important ingredient is in his mixture. The herbs pounded into theriac varied but every recipe included powdered dried viper. The mendicant seems to be wearing eye protection; vipers have been known to spit venom.

Opposite: The number of containers for theriac which survive until the present show just how widespread it was. It was an important medicine for 600 years, used by Arab doctors and lasting until Elizabethan times. The Age of Reason in the seventeenth century consigned it to the museums, where its containers are found today.

Some of the theriac containers are very attractive. This Delft jar from 1680 is decorated with St George slaying the dragon, implying that theriac will destroy disease in the same way. The jar is dated and labelled Theriaca Androm(icus).

The claims made for theriac were considerable. It was supposed to cure everything from the plague to syphilis. Theriac fell out of fashion as scientific discoveries produced genuine cures for the ills formerly treated by viper medicine.

Another popular ingredient in mediaeval medicine was unicorn horn. People believed in unicorns for many centuries, and the belief was reinforced by the narwhal tusks brought back by sailors, along with tales of mermaids. These ivory tusks were ground up to make very expensive but not very useful remedies.

Even more unlikely ingredients were found in goats and toads. Although toads are fairly common animals and many people saw them regularly, they were believed to have a magical stone in their heads that prevented poisons from taking effect. People in the Middle Ages, particularly those holding high office, went in constant fear of being poisoned. Some monarchs, like Catherine de Medici, had reputations as poisoners, giving gifts of poisoned gloves, according to legends. Anything that warded off poisoning was treasured, and these talismans included the toad stone and the bezoar stone, which came from the stomach of goats. What people thought they possessed when they had a bezoar or toad stone is anyone's guess, but these stones were bought for fabulous sums of money. An early example of a confidence trick!

Alternative Medicines Today

Alternative medicines, or complementary medicines as they are known to physicians, are an acknowledgement of the fact that cures are often brought about in inexplicable ways. After a period in which they were rather frowned upon, doctors now make use of some of the branches of medicine which were once regarded as "cranky". Some, as we have seen, are very old, and the herbal remedies are an important part of medical history.

Acupuncture is certainly the complementary medicine with the longest history, used today to relieve pain and as an anaesthetic if the patient cannot be given drugs.

Chiropractic and osteopathy are very similar in that they both manipulate the body, the difference being that chiropractitioners manipulate the spinal column to relieve pressure on nerves whilst osteopaths concentrate on pressure on the blood vessels as well. Osteopathy has registered practitioners who have followed a formal training and passed examinations to become qualified.

Homeopathy treats people on the principle that a small dose of a

Herbal remedies, like those used in homeopathy, have been used since prehistoric times. This nineteenth-century medicine chest is full of homeopathic remedies which were as much in use then as they are today, when they are manufactured on a commercial scale and packed in plastic tubes instead of these attractive vials.

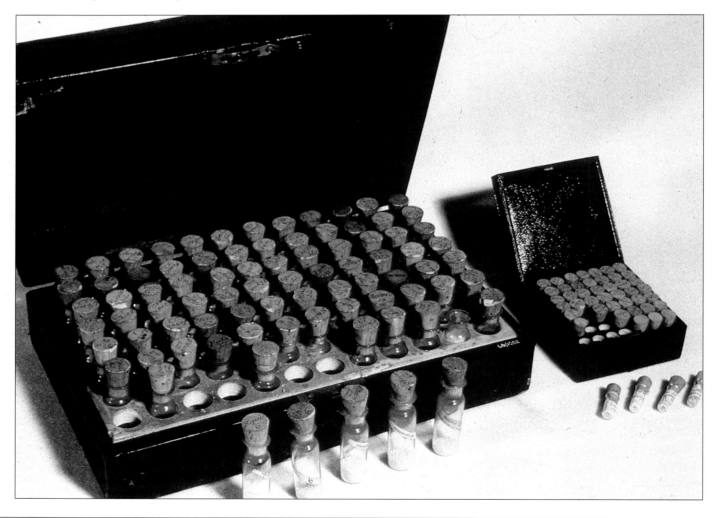

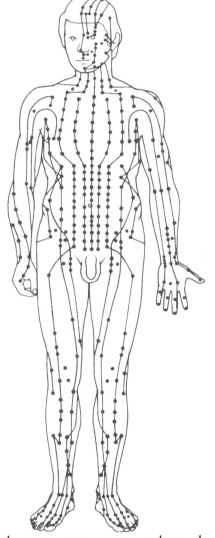

This is a modern acupuncture point chart, but it could easily be over 2,000 years old. There are charts very like this in ancient Chinese medical treatises. The lines in the diagram show the energy flows in the body and the points on the chart show where the energy flow can be stimulated to speed up recovery or aid relaxation. Acupuncture can be used as an anaesthetic in operations.

drug that produces the same symptoms as those shown by the patient will help the body to cure the ailment. It is the same principle as vaccination; if a dilute amount of something that causes the nose to run is introduced into the body, the body will produce the substances to combat the running nose. Homeopathy is a popular complementary medicine and practitioners can obtain a qualification from the International Academy of Homeopathy.

There are other alternative medicines which seem to help some people. Therapeutic touch, with slow sweeps of the practitioner's hands just above or lightly touching the body, claims to direct the patient's energies towards healing. Faith healing, or the laying on of hands, is similar. Reflexology is based on the theory that all the parts of the body are linked to areas in the feet. Reflexologists massage the feet of their patients to help headaches, backache, liver disorders and any other problem. Naturopathy combines homeopathy, acupuncture and herbal medicine with nutritional counselling to obtain their cures. Aromatherapy uses the oils, called essential oils, from a variety of plants to relieve pain and to calm stressed patients. Combined with massage, it is certainly very relaxing.

Chapter 9

CHEMISTRY AND PHARMACY

For centuries humans have used plants to help heal their ills, extracting the useful substances from the plant by various means. The study of the effect of chemicals from plants and from other sources on the human body is called pharmacology. Today pharmacology is the work of pharmaceutical chemists, and is part of a huge international pharmaceutical industry. The chemicals used in the drugs produced by the industry are made by chemical processes in most cases, although a few of them still come from plants; a far cry from the Stone Age, when plants supplied all the chemicals.

It was easy for the wise woman and the medicine man to search for the plant they wanted and extract the cure they wanted in quantities suitable for their tribe or their village. Then, as more people moved into the towns, the population increased and the numbers of people wanting medicines increased. The towns were built over the meadows and woods which had supplied the plants, and it became very difficult for townspeople to get the medicines that were still available in the countryside.

The wise women were replaced in towns by apothecaries, keeping shops in which dentists would pull teeth, and food was sold alongside the medicines. They would buy the plants needed from the countryside and would import more exotic cures, such as dried viper, cinchona bark, unicorn horn, ipecac and tobacco. Each apothecary had his own district, and so did not have to prepare huge amounts of the medicines that they made. By about 1800 the job done by apothecaries had been taken over by druggists and pharmacists. There are still apothecaries in Britain today, but they are usually doctors belonging to the Society of Apothecaries.

The druggists and pharmacists took over the dispensing of medicines as the apothecaries became doctors. As more research was carried out on the medicinal plants, the chemical formulae

Chemistry as a science began in the seventeenth century but chemists had little to do with medicine until the nineteenth century. This lithograph of 1841 by Daumier shows a chemist demonstrating the presence of arsenic in a compound. Arsenic in small doses is used in several medicines.

Hospitals once had their own dispensaries to make the medicines needed by the doctors. This photograph shows pharmaceutical technicians making quantities of drugs for use at St Bartholomew's Hospital in London in the 1920s. Today, drugs are bought from international pharmaceutical manufacturers.

Opposite: Patent medicine vendors used all the tricks of self-advertisement to sell their wares, some of which were actually harmful in those days before there were any laws controlling their content. Some tonic pills were made from soap with ginger and bitter aloes added. This music hall song of 1900 makes fun of the quack salesman's patter.

of the compounds which effected the cures were discovered and chemists began to try making them chemically. The Royal Pharmaceutical Society of Great Britain was founded in 1841 and was granted a Royal Charter in 1843. It inaugurated a school of pharmacy in 1842, which is now the School of Pharmacy of the University of London. It plays an important part in listing the many drugs produced by pharmaceutical companies, in publishing information on the isolation and identification of drugs, and in supplying information on drugs. Pharmaceutical chemists discover new drugs which are developed by different companies and under different names. These names are registered and published in the BP (British Pharmacopoeia), the USP (United States Pharmacopoeia) or the BPC (British Pharmaceutical Codex).

From Alchemy to Patent Medicines

Alchemists were the men who spent their lives trying to make gold from other metals and attempting to find the elixir of life that gave

immortality. They were the first chemists; they began the road that led to biochemistry and chemotherapy. Alchemists never did find out how to turn lead into gold, but they did perfect the techniques of distillation and isolation of acids, alcohol and metals, and they investigated sulphur and mercury. They handed on some fascinating names as well. Mercury was also known as 'seed of the dragon', 'dew', 'milk of the black cow', 'water of the moon', 'Scythian water' and 'water of silver'.

Through the next few centuries mercury was used to cure syphilis, the scourge of Europe and the disease which prevented Henry VIII from producing a healthy male heir (and possibly stopped Queen Elizabeth I from marrying). Mercury was not an effective cure, and syphilis was eventually conquered by penicillin. Apothecaries offered other cures, like guiacum wood, but syphilis remained as the worst of the sexually transmitted diseases until the arrival of HIV in the 1970s.

When the apothecaries began to retire as providers of medicines and their places were taken by druggists and pharmacists, medicines were more expensive. In America, unqualified men would make up medicines that were supposed to cure a variety of ills, and they toured in covered wagons, putting on a show and conning the audience into buying bottles of their cures. Some may have been based on genuine tonics made from herbs, but many were of no medicinal value at all.

In Britain, the migration of people from country to towns and the Industrial Revolution coincided with the changeover from

This woodcut of 1536 shows the interior of a pharmacist's shop. One assistant stirs a medicine while the other reaches for a jar. The pharmacist keeps an eye on the potion while talking to a physician. The jars all have air-tight seals 'to prevent stagnation or too ready escape of the odiferous principles'.

Ideas of being healthy change! When diets were bad and most poor people could not afford good food, fat people were thought to be healthy. This man, who would be considered overweight today, is used as part of a 'before and after' advertisement for J. Morison's pills. Before is demonstrated by the very thin version shown on the placard. This man would carry the placard through the streets advertising the pills.

apothecaries to pharmacists. Poorer people could not afford to go to doctors, and the first of the patent medicines appeared at prices nearer to the earnings of most people. People took brimstone and treacle, sulphur and molasses, castor oil, cod liver oil and similar doses if they appeared to be ailing. People were blistered with mustard plasters to get rid of cold or had their feet put into mustard baths, and cuts were treated with salt or iodine.

The first products of the pharmaceutical industry appeared in the 1890s. The advertisements can be seen in the magazines of the time. Beecham's Pills, which spread from Britain to America, contained ginger, aloes and soap. Not much use, one would think, but the placebo effect worked wonderfully! Carter's Little Liver Pills, Blue Pills, the list of these medicines was endless. Some may have had a little useful effect, some were useless, and a few were actually harmful. Patent medicines are still sold today, but now they are strictly controlled by laws in most countries and must have medicinal ingredients.

Drugs

A drug is any substance, produced from plants or from chemicals by humans, which is used for medicinal purposes. Camomile tea is as much a drug as heroin; it is not, however, a controlled drug. Controlled drugs are those that can be harmful. That excludes camomile tea, but certainly includes the highly addictive heroin.

Drugs work on the human body in one of five ways; they may have a physical effect, they may react with another chemical to neutralize it, they may take the place of another substance at its receptor, they may be included in a chemical in the body, or they may stop an enzyme from working.

The drugs that have a physical effect include an ointment to treat sunburnt skin, drugs to change the stools to help with treating bowel ailments, and plasma to replace lost blood or body fluids after an accident.

Neutralizing drugs can be as simple as sodium bicarbonate, taken to counteract excess stomach acid, or as complicated as the drugs that combine with mercury, lead and other poisonous heavy metals to make them harmless. Modern drugs in this class have been especially designed to neutralize other drugs, such as Digoxin, if they are taken in harmful quantities. Scientists are researching the production of antibodies to neutralize the poisons released by bacteria in the body.

The body is a giant chemical plant, and its simplest actions are the result of chemical changes. Any particular cell usually has a molecule designed as a kind of switch. The molecule is activated when another, which fits it exactly, is moved to it and bonds with it. There are drugs which produce exact replicas of the activating molecule which combine with the switch molecule and stop it working. It may be muscular contraction that is stopped by a muscle relaxing drug, or a drug which relaxes muscles in the lungs to allow easy breathing, or even a pain-killer like morphine. Morphine, properly used, is a pain-blocking drug, but it is also addictive and has to be used with great care.

The anti-cancer drugs used in chemotherapy work by becoming part of the cancer cells to stop them working so that they die. The cancer cells are growing and dividing very quickly, out of control.

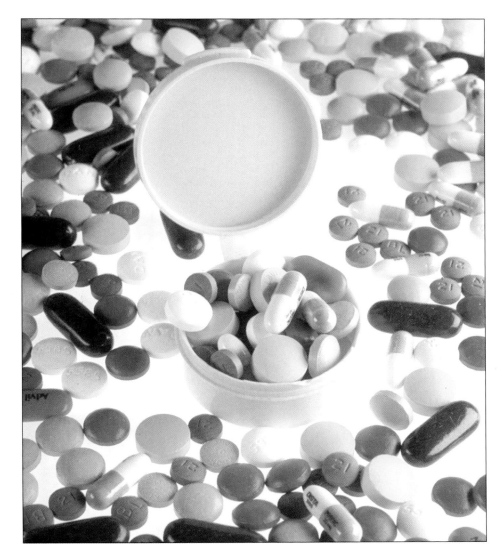

Some of the bewildering variety of drugs available today. There is no problem about taking the correct dose. The drugs come from the manufacturer weighed into pills and capsules, the amount shown clearly on the container. Some are pills; their dose works all at once. Others are in gelatinous capsules that release the drug in small continuous doses over some hours. These convenient packages contain drugs ranging from powerful pain-killers to controllers of cold symptoms. Supplied with these accurate packages of drugs, some can be bought without a prescription. For more powerful drugs, the doctor simply prescribes the correct number and gives the patient instructions about how many to take and how often to take them. Drugs cannot be adulterated with cheap ingredients and cannot be contaminated easily when they are sold in this form.

Because of the speed with which they grow and multiply, they take up the anti-cancer drugs more quickly than the normal cells, but normal cells do take them up as well, and they are affected too, which is why patients' hair falls out during chemotherapy.

The drugs that stop enzymes working properly include aspirin, penicillin and AZT, the antiviral drug used to treat AIDS. For example, penicillin stops the enzyme that forms the wall of a bacterial cell, so that the cell cannot form properly and dies.

These classes of drugs are used to fight infection, to treat malignant diseases such as cancer, to help musculoskeletal disorders such as gout and rheumatism, to help glandular disorders such as diabetes, to treat nervous disorders such as Parkinson's disease and depression, and to treat intestinal ailments such as ulcers, heart diseases and breathing disorders.

The drugs that fight infections actually attack the organisms that cause the diseases. The penicillins, tetracyclines, cephalosporins, aminoglycosides and sulphonamides are the antibiotics that attack bacteria; they are antibacterials. There are antiviral agents used to attack viruses such as the herpes that causes cold sores, antifungal agents to treat skin diseases like ringworm, and the antituberculous agents which attack the tuberculosis bacterium. Diseases such as malaria and amoebic dysentery are caused by protozoans, which are killed by antimalarial drugs, and amoebicides and trichomonacides.

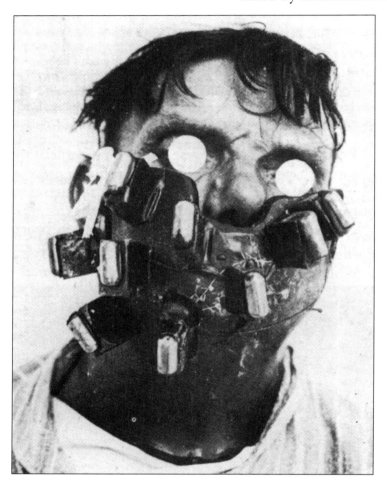

Cancer may be generally treated with drugs in chemotherapy but specific growths can be treated with radiotherapy. This extraordinary mask for radium treatment of cancer of the head and neck was in use in the 1920s. The masks were individually made for each patient and the sources of radium were mounted on it.

Malignant cancers are attacked by cytotoxic agents like doxorubicin and bleomycin (which kill cancer cells), antimetabolites, which stop the cells from working, and the Vinca alkaloids like vincristine.

Arthritis, rheumatism and similar diseases of muscles and bones may be treated by non-steroidal anti-inflammatory drugs, like salicyclate, or by aspirin. There are other drugs, such as acetic acid derivative, indolacetic acid derivative and oxicam, which do the same job as aspirin. Anti-rheumatics include gold salt, a very expensive treatment of rheumatism, and one of the blocking agents, penicillamine. Gout is kept under control with xanthine oxidase inhibitor.

There are many hypnotic, anxiolytic, antipsychotic, antidepressant and anticonvulsant drugs used to help nervous disorders. Severe diseases like schizophrenia can now be controlled with the help of these drugs, provided that they are taken regularly. Used sensibly, they help people – who would once have spent their lives in an institution – to live normally.

Asthma, an increasingly serious condition, is helped by the bronchodilators, drugs that open the airways in the lungs to help sufferers to breathe. Anti-anginal drugs like nitrates and beta-blockers help to control spasms of the heart, keeping it beating regularly; and drugs can now be used to cure ulcers.

With this inventory it is hardly surprising that some diseases have disappeared, although some of the Victorian diseases have re-emerged in Britain at the end of the twentieth century as homeless people have returned to the poor diets and living conditions of the last century. Tuberculosis has re-appeared, showing how easy it is for disease to attack those who are not able to take care of themselves satisfactorily.

Tuberculosis can be eradicated again quickly with the help of modern drugs, provided that the people living in these poor conditions can be found and treated, and that the financial aid needed for treatment is forthcoming. It is also important that public health and a good diet keep individuals healthy. The drugs have helped to combat the diseases of the world, but prevention is better than cure, and healthy living has done as much if not more than drugs to get rid of the life-threatening diseases.

Misuse of Drugs

Unhappily, when people read of drugs today, it is not usually because of the amazing transformation in health of a large part of the human population, but because of the way in which sections of the population misuse them. Many drugs are addictive, and addicts will

The invention of the hypodermic syringe made it much easier for doctors to administer drugs. Introducing any substance into the blood system was extremely difficult before intravenous injection was made possible. This shows an old-fashioned hypodermic syringe with a metal needle. These were blunted by too much use, and made injections very painful, but they would be changed at intervals. Drug abusers also use hypodermic syringes, because the drug takes effect more quickly if introduced into the blood-stream. Before the advent of AIDS the habit of sharing hypodermic needles was unhygienic, but not lethal. The needles transferred blood from one person to another and carried the HIV infection with the blood. This resulted in the invention of plastic, throw-away hypodermic syringes designed for once-only use. These are given away free to registered drug addicts to help stop the spread of AIDS. They are also used by diabetics; the fine, sharp points make injections almost painless.

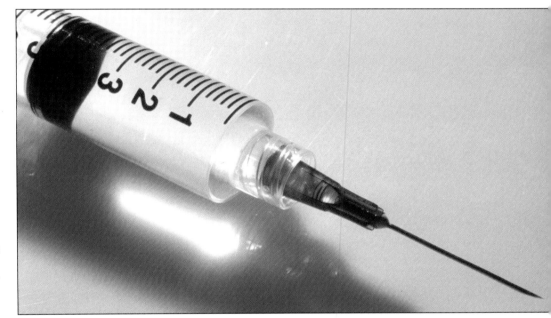

go to any lengths to get the drugs which have become part of the chemistry of their bodies. With a regular supply they do not pose a problem, but if they cannot afford to keep pace with their increasing dependence, they will turn to crime to finance their habit.

When doctors are talking about drug abuse, they actually use the words substance abuse; alcohol, solvents and even loud music and violence can all be included in substance abuse. Strictly speaking, alcohol is a drug. A little alcohol has a medicinal effect on a body and some medicines include it, but drunkenness is a form of drug abuse. Humans found out how to ferment different plants in prehistoric times, and alcohol was probably used in religious ceremonies, as it is today. Too much alcohol will kill, damaging the liver to the point at which it can no longer function properly. Too much alcohol also damages the life of the abuser, spoiling relationships and causing irresponsibility. Too much alcohol combined with driving a car is a murderous combination which is punishable by law. It would be short-sighted to exclude alcohol from drug abuse.

When tobacco first arrived in Europe it was regarded as a useful drug. Culpeper wrote in 1653 in his *Complete Herbal*: 'Tobacco is found by good experience to help to spit out tough phlegm from the stomach, chest and lungs...the seed is very effectual to expel the tooth ache...The juice is also used to kill lice in children's heads.' It was also believed to cure worms. Tobacco was imported from the West Indies, where it was prepared by 'stringing and rolling', as seen in this illustration from Pomet's *Histoire Generale des Drogues* published in 1696. It was discovered in the 1960s that tobacco was carcinogenic; today, smoking kills more people every year than traffic and murders.

Tobacco is another substance not usually regarded as a drug, but which has medicinal uses in small quantities. It is certainly addictive; witness the misery endured by someone trying to break the habit by giving up smoking. Too much tobacco is another killer, this time through increased risk of heart and blood circulation diseases and through the damage to the lungs.

More conventional drugs have been misused for a long time too. Opium has been smoked for centuries; opium dens, where people lie on bunk beds lost in an opium daze, were the ultimate degradation in Victorian novels. Drinking a mixture of laudanum and wine was fashionable; the poet Coleridge was addicted to that combination. Addicts also ate opium. Modern opium abusers no longer use opium, they use the derivative morphine. The invention of the hypodermic needle made it possible to inject morphine into the body directly, to obtain faster results. Sadly, some addictions began when soldiers were given morphine to ease the pain of wounds received in battles, beginning with the American Civil War in the 1860s. Addiction to injecting morphine and its derivative, heroin, was actually known as the soldier's disease.

Today, injecting morphine or heroin with shared hypodermic needles carries the added danger of contracting AIDS. The addict community is one in which the HIV virus is present, and addicts are issued with clean needles in an attempt to stop the disease spreading further.

There is treatment for morphine and heroin addiction, but it takes great determination on the part of the addict. The painful withdrawal symptoms which were a part of the cure can now be helped by a synthetic opiate, methadone, which takes the place of morphine in the body's chemistry and is not as destructive as morphine. The dose is then reduced slowly until the body can survive without it again.

Opium and its derivatives are certainly not the only addictive drugs. Coca has been used for a long time, particularly in South America. It is cocaine, the extract of the coca leaves, which is the drug sniffed by celebrities to help them perform when they are tired. The latest form of cocaine is the new crystalline "crack", so called because of the noise it makes when it is heated, and its use is becoming an increasing problem.

Other new drugs include the amphetamines and lysergic acid, or LSD. The problem with LSD is that it can be made easily by a reasonably knowledgeable chemist, but because of this can vary considerably in strength and purity. It is possible for people to die from uncontrolled LSD, sold as Ecstasy to teenagers. There is no way of controlling the dose when it is made illegally.

The 1960s brought a wave of drugs such as marihuana (pot, grass, Acapulco gold etc.) which people smoked as cigarettes for the hallucinogenic effects. Mescaline, made from cactus, and psilocybin, made from mushrooms, were used for the same reason. These are not as addictive as coca and opium; takers may enjoy the effects, but the chemicals do not affect the body chemistry to the same degree, and so they are regarded as soft drugs. The addiction is mental rather than an actual, physical one.

In recent years another form of drug abuse has appeared, involving athletes. Bodybuilding drugs such as the steroids will improve an athlete's performance in competitions. Glucose for quick energy was always a useful aid, but the ethics of using drugs to improve performance has only arrived with the increasing commercialism of athletics. Top performers become wealthy and the temptation to use drugs to become a top performer is a great one. The organizers of sporting events now do rigorous drugs tests on athletes to make sure that they are not using artificial aids.

Looking at the abuse of the marvellous work done by generations of medical men and women is a depressing finish to an account of how humans have fought diseases through the centuries. It is also typical of humans, in that they invent something wonderful and then discover a way of doing something dreadful with it. The medical profession must now find ways of making sure that the human population does not overrun the planet and destroy it. An effective birth control drug, without dangerous side effects, is an essential part of future research.

Humans have worked through the ages to stop people dying of wounds, disease and malnutrition. Physicians, surgeons, apothecaries and medical researchers have made it possible to live longer and do more. Once upon a time people died at about the age of 40; it is now quite normal to live until 70, and centenarians are not as rare as they used to be. With more people having more babies who survive in larger numbers and live longer, it will soon be very important indeed to make sure that there is room on this planet for humans, and for all the other plants and animals that existed in the biosphere for 4,000 million years before humans turned up.

Time Chart of Some Medical Practices

20th CENTURY	Aboriginal medicine Wart charming		Acupuncture	Drugs Contraceptives Penicillin	Surgery Open heart surgery Asepsis	Technology ITU ECG	Anti-septics	Public Health
19th CENTURY					Lister Pasteur	X-rays	Anaesthetics	Clean water Public sewers
18th CENTURY						Vaccination by Jenner		
17th CENTURY		The reign of Theriac			Harvey discovers germs	Microscope		
16th CENTURY				Quinine	Ligaturing blood vessels			Invention of water closet
15th CENTURY				Drugs				
12th-14th Centuries								
1,000 AD								Roman baths
1st Century AD								Greek baths
1,000 BC			Acupuncture		Tracheostomy by Galen			Indian sewers
2,000 BC					Metal instruments			
10,000 BC	Spells and witchcraft				Trepanning Surgery			

Index